D1387458

New Problems in Medical Ethics

EDITED IN ENGLISH BY

DOM PETER FLOOD

O.S.B., B.A., M.D., M. CH., J.C.L.,

BARRISTER-AT-LAW

TRANSLATED BY MALACHY GERARD CARROLL

NUMBER I

ARTIFICIAL INSEMINATION

DEATH

THE MERCIER PRESS

CORK, IRELAND

First published in English by
The Mercier Press Ltd.,
4 Bridge Street, Cork, Ireland

Nihil Obstat: Eduardus Mahoney, S.T.D.
Censor Deputatus

Imprimatur: † Edwardus Myers,
Archiepiscopus Beroeensis
et Coadiutor Westmonasteriensis

Printed in the Netherlands
by N.V. Drukkerij Bosch, Utrecht

Contents

Artificial Insemination

EDITOR'S NOTE

In 1934 Père Riquet, then chaplain to the medical students and doctors in Paris, decided to launch a review of medical deontology called, the 'Cahiers Laënnec,' which would describe the problems and 'cases of conscience' that arise in medical practice and expound their solution on the basis of Catholic moral principles. This venture was crowned with immediate success and continued until interrupted by World War II. After the war, the review was revived by Père Riquet's successor, Père Larère, S.J., and at the request of the 'Mouvement international des Intellectuels Catholiques de Pax Romana,' the 'Cahiers Laënnec' became the official review of the Medical Secretariat. It would be unjust not to mention the older 'Conference Laënnec' founded in 1875 by the Jesuit Fathers in Paris with similar objectives which, after the First World War, was to inspire the formation of the well-known body called, 'les Amis de Laënnec.'

It is our intention in presenting this translation to English speaking readers, clerical and medical, to demonstrate what has been done by these efforts to enunciate the rule of Christian principles in the practice of our colleagues in France, whose difficulties so nearly approach our own although their approach to them from the scientific angle may not always be the same as ours. Each contributor has presented the problem under examination from his own standpoint and though we do not always find ourselves in agreement with the views expressed, nevertheless their expression has been necessary to a clear understanding of the difficulty as it appears to them and as it requires solution according to the moral principles applicable to the case.

EDITOR

EDITOR'S FOREWORD

The subject treated of in the following articles has acquired very considerable importance in the study of the correct ethical approach to the problems of modern medical practice. Large scale experiments made in the case of American soldiers and their wives during the recent war, as well as the success claimed by certain well known hospital clinics, both in this country and abroad, which have treated sterility, more especially when the husband was either absolutely or relatively sterile or impotent, by the intra-vaginal introduction of semen obtained from their husbands or from donors unknown to the parties concerned, have given publicity to this procedure. At least one such clinic claims almost 100 per cent successful pregnancies from this method and guarantees that the donors are young men of unimpeachable medical and family history, both from the physical and psychological point of view; at the same time they are stated to be a judicious blend of brain and brawn – *mens sana in corpore sano* – though one might perhaps wonder whether any completely normal minded young man would willingly and regularly lend himself to such a practice for a fee. Be that as it may, the practice is on the increase and there are not wanting those who, in perfect good faith, argue in favour of the advantages that they claim attend it, pointing out that hitherto childless couples are thus enabled to have children that are at least half theirs and that the donors concerned have the satisfaction of being the fathers of many hundreds and, perhaps, thousands of children unknown to them. Although it is true that the dangers of inbreeding in small communities are recognised and that, for this reason, some clinics will use the same donors only for a limited period of time, usually several years, there can be no adequate guarantee against such dangers.

It must be obvious that the existence of this practice raises certain questions both for the parties directly concerned themselves, and for those whose duties as doctors, medical students, nurses, and others bring them into contact with such departments. This problem is not altogether new and a great deal of theological discussion has taken place in regard to the moral values concerned. This led to the simple condemnation of artificial fecundation by the Holy Office in 1897, no details or methods being specifically mentioned, and culminated in the Allocution of Pius XII in 1949. Certain aspects of the problem have therefore ceased to be controversial; it is never permitted to inseminate a woman with semen from a man not her husband – within marriage, one may never perform acts wrong in themselves, no matter how legitimate their intended end; in a word, the end no matter how good in itself, can never justify the use of means, unlawful in themselves, to its attainment. Hence it is clear that no wife may be inseminated with semen obtained from the husband outside lawful coitus, i.e. by a lawful marital act which places the male semen where it should be normally placed, *intra vaginam*. The Pope does not exclude certain artificial methods intended to facilitate the natural act nor does he necessarily exclude methods which are designed to enable the marital act, when performed naturally, to attain its end. We think that the measures sometimes adopted in cases of epi- or hypospadias and certain cases of physical disproportion, come under the first heading and those which assist the semen to pass from its natural place of deposition to a site farther up, come under the second heading, always providing that the semen is placed in the vagina by a normal marital act. We think such aids assist the generative function of the woman and merely assist the procreative act, already completed naturally, to attain its end. Though so great an authority as Gemelli does not hold this opinion, we think that the majority of modern theologians are in agreement with our view. Creusen seems to think that the methods to which we have just referred have neither been approved nor condemned in the Papal Allocution but if, in fact, the Pope did not refer to these methods, it is difficult to see to what other procedure his statements have reference, but in any case the principles he lays down are readily applicable to these cases and do not seem to us to invalidate our conclusions.

As to doctors, nurses, and other attendants taking part in the work of such clinics, we think that the rules, governing their attendance at morally condemned operations in the operating theatre, must apply; in brief, this is to say that they must not give an active proximate co-operation to the work of the clinic. The case of the pathologist is more difficult to decide and the problem must be settled in each individual case having regard to his precise duties in the matter.

If, as some research workers have envisaged, it ever becomes possible to introduce an ovum from one woman into another so that it may be fertilised in her by the natural act of her husband, this will never be permissible. The external products of the genital glands, testis and ovary, are intended to be used lawfully only within matrimony, and therein through the means of the natural marital act. The partners can neither alienate their rights in this matter nor acquire any right to the secretions of other persons. As the Pope so clearly says, 'the natural and Divine positive Laws are such that the procreation of a new life may be the fruit of marriage alone.' This is the Divine Law and not just a disciplinary measure imposed by the Church as so many non-Catholics seem to think.

Artificial insemination cannot validate any marriage which is already invalid in the sight of God by reason of the impediment of impotence, nor are the children of such a procedure legitimate. It is of interest to note that no such child would be regarded as legitimate in English law nor in that of Canada or France where, indeed, the receipt of the active element from a donor, other than the husband, is held to be adultery on the part of the wife.

EDITOR

MEDICAL ASPECTS OF ARTIFICIAL INSEMINATION

Artificial insemination is the introduction of sperm into the interior of the female genital organs, otherwise than by sexual intercourse.

It is carried out with the husband's sperm when an obstacle exists to its introduction or to the ascension of the fertilising elements.

It is carried out with the sperm of a donor when the husband is sterile, or when procreation by him is considered undesirable.

Preliminary investigations

Artificial insemination is therefore envisaged only in certain well defined and clear cases, and after a whole series of examinations both of the husband and the wife has been carried out.

One of the most important discoveries made, as a result of recent researches, is the fact that the man is responsible in at least 35 per cent of cases of conjugal sterility (20 per cent complete azoospermia, 15 per cent at least of serious and often incurable asthenospermia).

The diagnosis of masculine sterility can be theoretically established in two ways – direct or indirect.

The *direct method* is the microscopic examination of the sperm, collected by masturbation or by interrupted intercourse, in a very dry beaker. (Condoms are not to be used, because they falsify results.)

Any competent laboratory should be able to give a correct result stating –

1. The quantity of the sperm (normally 3 to 6 c.c.).
2. The number of spermatozoa per c.c. (normally more than 60 millions).
3. The number of duly mobile spermatozoa (normally more than two-thirds between 1 hour and 3 hours after emission).
4. The number of spermatozoa present which are abnormal in form (normally less than 20 per cent).

Absolute sterility is established when, after tests carried out over some months, spermatozoa are never found (azoospermia).

More or less profoundly affected fertility is established when the sperm is of bad quality (oligo-asthenospermia) especially if this quality has degenerated at each successive examination.

The direct method leaves little room for doubt as to the value of the sperm at the time the experiment is made; and examinations yielding constantly bad results mean that there is little hope.

The *indirect method* comprises the examination of spermatozoa in the interior of the genital organs of the woman after sexual intercourse.

If the examination is not made in the first half-hour after intercourse, the spermatozoa found in the vagina are usually dead, and therefore no conclusions of any value can be reached as to their quality.

Of greater interest and *always indispensable* is the examination of the penetration of the spermatozoa into the secretions of the uterine cervix some hours after sexual intercourse. This penetration is necessary to fecundation.

But this penetration is not easily effected except during several days in each month, generally the three to five days around the date of *ovulation* which usually occurs a fortnight before the period. That the examination may yield results, therefore, it must coincide with the period of fertility, which can be calculated, apart from the calendar, by a study of the morning temperature chart and the appearance of the secretion of the cervix which should be limpid and viscous.

In these conditions, if sexual intercourse has taken place the previous evening or the same day, mobile spermatozoa, in greater or lesser numbers, should be found in the cervical secretion. This shows beyond all doubt that the husband possesses mobile spermatozoa, and that the cervical secretions are favourable to them.

Is it possible to use this indirect method of examination, in order to judge the value of the husband's sperm? Yes and no.

In the first place, it frequently happens that the cervical secretions do not present all the qualities required, and that, consequently, it is not possible to draw any conclusions from the absence of spermatozoa within them. It is desirable, however, to discover the value of the husband's sperm, before submitting the wife to painful and even somewhat dangerous investigation.

Moreover, even if the secretion appears to be perfect, the results are lacking somewhat in precision when compared with those reached by the direct method. According to a comparative study by Mme. Palmer in the School of Puericulture, it is possible to accept that –

(a) if mobile spermatozoa are found, it is a 90 per cent chance that the sperm is normal in quality, but the possibility of oligospermia is not ruled out. (Many specialists hold that quantitative insufficiency is a cause of marked diminution of fertility);

(b) if spermatozoa are not found, there is a 90 per cent chance that the sperm is frankly abnormal (azoospermia or oligoasthenospermia);

(c) if immobile spermatozoa only are found, the direct examination of the sperm is necessary in order to establish whether this immobility is due to the bad quality of the sperm or to some inimical quality of the cervical secretion.

In practice, therefore, the indirect proof can be regarded as sufficient when it is clearly positive (i.e. when there are numerous spermatozoa of normal morphology). All other cases require the direct examination of the sperm, before investigations are made on the wife.

If the examination of the sperm shows it to be normal, whereas there were no mobile spermatozoa in the cervical secretions, it becomes necessary to study and to treat the cervix in order that the spermatozoa may be able to penetrate. In cases of persistent failure, it may be considered necessary to carry out insemination with the sperm of the husband.

Sterility of masculine origin

Sterility of masculine origin can be traced either to an obstacle in the spermatic ducts (which can be cured by a delicate but mild operation in about 25 per cent of cases); or to a fault in the manufacture of spermatozoa by the testicles – a more or less serious fault which may even lead to the complete destruction of the power to produce spermatozoa.

In cases of azoospermia, the diagnosis between these two great causes and the condition of the power to produce spermatozoa, can be exactly established by a biopsy.

The results to date from the treatment of cases of azoospermia, and oligo-asthenospermia through failure in spermatogenesis, are far from brilliant (perhaps 10 per cent); but, if the generative cells are not altered on biopsy, the ultimate possibility of an improvement can clearly not be ruled out.

In practice, however, it must be admitted that the present prognosis of masculine cases of sterility is sufficiently serious; and that, if correct medical treatment, in conjunction with physical and intellectual repose and a more enlightened hygiene, has effected no improvement after two years, the only solution seems to be adoption or insemination with the sperm of a donor.

Now, many couples are averse to the adoption of a child, because they fear that it will have some blemish, and they prefer insemination which will give them a child that is at least half theirs, and whose progenitor is presumed to have been suitably chosen by the doctor.

Indications for insemination with the husband's sperm
Insemination with the husband's sperm may be indicated in the following cases –

(*a*) When *natural intra-vaginal insemination is impossible*, either because of a physical anomaly of the husband (hypospadias) or of the wife (stenosis and/or a vaginal membrane); or because of functional troubles (premature ejaculation, vaginismus).

(*b*) When *natural ascension of the spermatozoa in the uterus is impossible*, after the failure of treatment for endocervicitis or for causal cervical stenosis.

Here it must be noticed that a mucus which would be penetrated by virulent spermatozoa, may not be penetrated by a somewhat asthenic sperm. I have carried out two observations of pregnancy by insemination with sperms which were somewhat oligo-asthenospermic.

(*c*) A 'war' indication has been established by the Americans – that of the transport by air of the sperm of husbands fighting in the Pacific, when it was not known whether they would be there for months or for years. Many such long range inseminations have been successfully carried out.

Indications for insemination with the sperm of a donor

Artificial insemination with the sperm of a donor may be indicated either when the husband is absolutely sterile, or when there are grave medical reasons which make procreation by the husband undesirable.

1. Sterility of the husband

If the husband's sterility is due to obstruction of the seminal ducts, he is always invited to undergo an operation which is quite a mild one. If his desire for paternity is sincere, he will agree readily. When this fails, insemination by a donor should be considered.

If the husband's sterility is due to a deficiency in spermatogenesis, and biopsy of the testicles has shown that the generative cells are very seriously injured, the indication, though less absolute, is medically little open to discussion.

2. Contra-indications for procreation by the husband

There are a certain number of hereditary affections (malformations, psychoses) whose existence in the husband or his forebears renders procreation highly undesirable.

There are also the cases of erythro-blastosis of the newly born, linked with the rhesus factor. If there have been two consecutive deaths through this complication, it is almost certain that every other pregnancy with the husband for procreator will end in the same disaster. If the couple wish to have a child, therefore, artificial insemination must be performed with the sperm of an Rh negative donor.

Conditions for the success of artificial insemination

Experience of artificial insemination of the wife shows that it rarely succeeds the first time, and that it is often necessary to repeat the operation several times over several consecutive months in order to achieve the desired success.

In order to succeed, the following conditions must be fulfilled –

1. The wife must have normal genital organs with normal functioning

If there is obturation of a fallopian tube, it is desirable to verify by coelioscopy whether there are adhesions on the other side. If there are not, it may be hoped that ovulation will take place on the permeable side, though it cannot be ascertained in what month that may happen.

2. The sperm must be of good quality

Insemination with a sperm of doubtful quality is nearly always without effect. Some attempts can be made with the sperm of an oligo-spermic husband; but if the sperm shows several other anomalies, failure is probable.

Where insemination by a donor takes place it is clearly required that a sperm of very good quality should be used, and that it should be verified every time before use.

3. Insemination must be performed as near as possible to the moment of ovulation

It is probable that the ovum is capable of being fertilised only during a period of twelve hours, and the spermatozoa introduced into the female organism keep their fecundating power for probably 24 to 26 hours at most. If there is any doubt, therefore, about the exact date, it becomes necessary to repeat the injections every 48 hours during the period which is regarded as fertile.

If the wife has very regular periods, it can be taken for granted that ovulation occurs on the fifteenth day before the date of her next period, and insemination can be performed on the seventeenth and the fifteenth day before that date the first month, on the sixteenth and fourteenth day before that date the second month, etc.

If her periods do not occur with such regularity, the temperature chart and the study of the cervical secretion can be used to determine the moment when the favourable phase is probably ended.

4. The sperm must be sufficiently fresh and sufficiently concentrated

Generally, however, it is preferable to wait until the sperm liquefies, a process which will take 10 to 30 minutes according to the circumstances.

It is important that the sperm should not have been submitted to any rise in temperature. (It very quickly loses its fecundating power at 40°, and it keeps it for several days at 5°.) Neither should it be exposed to any harmful chemical influence, condoms being deplorable in this connection; and it is because water is equally harmful, that the sperm ought to be collected directly in a glass beaker, dry and sterilised by heat.

Experience of insemination of domestic animals has shown that the sperm can be diluted in the ratio of one part sperm to ten parts special glucose solution without excessive loss of fecundating power, and thus a syringe can be used for the impregnation of several of the female animals. Diluting is rarely indicated (perhaps for certain over-viscous sperms) in conditions of human artificial insemination.

Generally speaking, the most favourable moment for using the human sperm is between the 30th minute and the third hour after emission.

If the use must be postponed beyond that time, the sperm ought to be placed in a refrigerator at 5° in order –

(a) to avoid microbial pollution in the sperm;

(b) to prevent the spermatozoa from using up their potential power of motion. The refrigeration should be gradual, and the return to the temperature at which it is to be used should also be gradual.

5. A preliminary report does not seem to increase the chances of success.

6. The technique must avoid all risk of inflammatory accidents.

The instruments and the technique used should be aseptic, but no antiseptic must be used.

If the cervical mucus is normal and penetrable by the spermatozoa, the simplest and best technique is intra-cervical insemination. The woman is placed in the gynaecological position, the table is tilted backwards a little, and the cervix is well exposed by a speculum. The sperm is then instilled or projected in two or three spurts into the interior of the cervix and into the mucus there. A large part flows back into the vaginal cul-de-sac.

The speculum is taken away, and the patient is placed in the reverse position for a quarter of an hour, during which her cervix is being soaked in the sperm which was collected in the cul-de-sac at the rear of the vagina.

If the cervical mucus is abnormal, it should be squeezed out thoroughly with the valves of the speculum, the cervical cavity should be sponged with a small sterile tampon, and an injection made just beyond the isthmus, but with a slow release which should be continued while gradually withdrawing the cannula. A sudden injection into the bodily cavity provokes a uterine spasm, causes severe pain, and diminishes the chances of success. It also increases the chances of infectious complications.

After a quarter of an hour, the woman can resume her normal occupation without diminishing the chances of fecundation.

Medical conditions required in a donor

The first condition is clearly that he should be in good health and free from all transmittable diseases, venereal or otherwise. Hence the reason why many doctors have recourse to blood donors, who are tested periodically for these things.

The donor must be studied from the point of view of heredity (malformation, psychoses in forebears or collaterals). Some doctors advise the exclusive use of donors who are more than thirty-five years old (the majority of hereditary psychoses disappearing before that age), and of subjects who have fine and healthy children.

It is equally desirable that the donor should resemble the husband in physical and racial qualities. It is worth while to take precautions lest parents with dark eyes have a fair child with blue eyes. If possible, the intellectual and moral quality of the donor should be equal or superior to that of the parents.

As a matter of fact, the majority of American doctors whom I have interviewed on this subject, use students from their own medical services or laboratories, and easily find the necessary volunteers in these services.

Psycho-social conditions

A certain number of conditions of a psycho-social order are absolutely necessary in order to avoid all unpleasant consequences.

1. The donor must not know who the couple are

The best way of securing this is that the donor should have no occasion to come into the doctor's waiting-room, and that the doctor should perform the insemination simply as one of several other gynaecological consultations.

2. The couple should not know who is the donor

This aims especially at avoiding the danger of eventual transfer of affection, and also of recriminations when the offspring is not perfect.

3. Every third party not bound by the medical secret should be told nothing about the operation

The child's future may depend on this, both from the material point of view (heritage) and from the moral (he should have no doubts about his parentage). The family and the family of the donor must be told nothing whatever about it. Weisman points out that all these conditions of secrecy are more easily secured in a city than in a little provincial town.

4. There must be certainty about the deep and persistent desire of the couple and the stability of their home

If either party shows the least sign of lukewarmness, on no pretext should they be granted a request which they may later regret having made. They should be made to repeat their request many times before artificial insemination by a donor is attempted.

There must be equal certainty about the stability of the home, in a country where divorce is easy and frequent. The child would most certainly be the victim of such a separation.

An adequately prolonged psychological study of the couple seems therefore desirable before consent is given for artificial insemination by a donor.

Juridical precautions

Is it equally necessary to take precautions of a juridical order? There are two opposed attitudes in this matter –

(*a*) Those who practise insemination by a donor in rare cases only, and after careful psychological investigation, consider that all documents are useless in these cases if the precautions of secrecy previously indicated have been taken.

(*b*) Others, on the contrary, such as Seymour and Weisman, are of opinion that sufficient precautions can never be taken. I summarise the precautions advised by Weisman.

For the protection of the doctor, he requires –

1. Written consent, in duplicate, certified by an attorney and bearing the fingerprints of the husband and of the wife.

2. Written consent of the donor, lest he should later complain that sperm given by him for a simple examination was otherwise used, or lest he should claim a right of paternity if he got to know the identity of the recipient.

3. The written consent of the donor's wife.

For the protection of the mother (against an eventual action for adultery), he requires –

1. The written consent of the husband, as above.

2. The delivery of the woman should be performed by another doctor who can sign the birth certificate without the least scruple.

For the protection of the child (so that his right to heritage cannot be contested by other possible heirs), he thinks that more than one precaution should be taken.

As regards heritage, the legitimacy of the child is indeed open to discussion. If other heirs got wind of the manner in which the child was conceived, they could theoretically oppose his right, if they succeeded in proving that it was impossible for the father to have been the parent. Thus, in 1939, the legists of the 'American Medical Association' considered that this danger was no fiction, and that the husband would act prudently by assuring in every way the material future of the child, either by a policy of assurance, or even, 'setting aside all considerations of pride and delicacy' (*sic*), by a process of legal adoption.

For the protection of the donor

Finally, Weisman thinks it prudent that the paper authorising insemination should contain a phrase exonerating the donor from all responsibility of every kind. The donor should also keep a copy of his wife's (*sic*) authorisation.

The doctor must seal all these papers and put them in his strong-box. If the doctor dies, only his attorney should have access to the sealed papers, and these should be accompanied by a note directing that they are to be put in the hands of such-and-such a doctor who is familiar with questions concerning insemination and with their medico-legal aspects.

(*c*) In France, by reason of the obligation which binds the doctor to *absolute professional secrecy*, these precautions are of no great value since he has not the right to use them. For predominantly psychological reasons, however, it is desirable to have the written authorisation of the husband and wife stating that, as they desire greatly to have children and have not succeeded in spite of all their efforts and of the treatment they have undergone, they seek insemination with the sperm of a donor chosen by the doctor and not known to them, it being understood that the donor chosen will be healthy and without any blemish ascertainable by present medical processes.

DR. RAOUL PALMER
*Chef des Travaux de gynecologie
à la Faculté de Médecine de Paris*

ARTIFICIAL INSEMINATION AND
THE LAW OF FRANCE

Artificial insemination took by surprise the Law of France, codified one hundred and forty years ago. The Napoleonic legislation had always considered the insemination of the woman as connected with coitus. It was never concerned with what might happen to its provisions if one of these elements were separated from the other. It is therefore the spirit as well as the letter of these provisions that must be consulted, in order to bring their content into line with new problems.

Some main ideas, even when they are not formulated, underlie clearly the rules of the French civil penal code in matters of sexual relations, and especially of insemination. Arising from the Natural Law, they are in a sense anterior to Christianity. In their development, however, they have been profoundly marked with its imprint which continues to set its seal on our juridical civilisation. They combine a civil deposit, a humanist deposit, a social deposit.

The civil deposit comprises the ideas of contract and possession. Sexual intercourse is here regarded from the angle of the most complete and most exclusive possession of one being by another. This possession corresponds to a right, itself born of a contract. All legislations of history have known this contract – marriage, which gives to one human being the right to the possession of another. In the primitive Roman city, such right was not far from being identified with the appropriation of the woman by the man. Christianity, which has founded the modern matrimonial law, has elevated it to a mutual and irrevocable giving of self which each spouse makes to the other. In this, it has recovered its human deposit.

The latter marks the transcendent value of the procreative act, and links it closely and intimately with what concerns human dignity. At the same time, this point of view completes the preceding. What man gives, in the sex act, is his most intimate and most sacred possession, which he cannot sell but only give, which cannot be taken from him against his will without 'violating him.' For it is he alone who can dispose of it. It is there that his liberty is most indivisibly joined to his dignity as a man.

Finally, the social point of view is also essentially concerned with the procreative character of the sex act. It is by this act that human society is perpetuated. The very existence of this society depends on it, and that is why society cannot be indifferent to it. To assure its future, it must even see beyond procreation, and ensure the nurture and upbringing of the child, which leads it to envisage for the child the provision, not only of a mother, but of a father also. Hence the social importance of the fidelity of the married woman, and the rule: *'pater is est quem nuptiae demonstrant.'*

These three ideas will clarify the sense of the texts which they inspire. However cut and polished the texts may be, these ideas will allow them to be adapted to new problems. This adaptation must be made successively to the two great branches of law which concern artificial insemination: penal law and civil law.

1. Penal law

The insemination of the woman can be done either with her consent or as imposed by force.

In the second case, does it qualify for being listed as rape, to be punished under art. 332 of the Penal Code?

In our opinion, we can have no doubts about it, because, in rape, it is not the coitus itself which the law essentially forbids, but the violation of what a woman regards as her most intimate and most reserved possession – the violation of what her liberty alone can give. Now, a woman's intimacy is just as much seized by forcing her into an unwilling artificial insemination as by forcing coitus on her against her will. And the social consequences of the first of these acts are not less serious than those of the second.

If the woman has consented to insemination, the penal law appears to take no interest in such an act, when the woman is not married; because the necessity of keeping its interventions within the limits of efficacy has caused criminal law to renounce punishment in a general way, for sexually immoral acts. It concerns itself with such a case only when certain determined circumstances accentuate its anti-social character and allow of its being qualified as crime.

Such would be the case, for example, if artificial insemination had been performed in public, as this would then constitute a public act of indecency (art. 330). The supposed scientific character of the experiment would certainly not cover the offence.

But it is above all in matters of adultery that the question of a repressive qualification can arise.

It is well known that the penal code distinguishes between the adultery of the husband and the adultery of the wife, because the latter is socially much more serious since it alone is capable of causing confusion in the case of procreation, and of causing the children of the intruder to be deceitfully admitted into the legal family. Thus the adultery is in itself punishable, because it is by nature anti-social. That of the husband is not, unless it is accompanied by a scandalous breach of faith: the keeping of a concubine in the conjugal home (art. 336 to 339 C. pen.).

This difference and the idea which inspires it, allow us to appreciate from the point of view of adultery the penal qualification of artificial insemination.

Even if it is the semen of a married man which is used on a woman other than his wife, this practice is not, any more than the adultery of the husband, legally punishable.

But if a married woman has herself voluntarily fecundated with the semen of a man other than her husband, or even if she attempts this artificial fecundation, she leaves herself open to punishment by the law. She runs a serious risk of bringing an intruder into the family and deceitfully imposing that intruder on her husband who is disarmed, as we have seen, by the maxim: '*Pater is est quem nuptiae demonstrant.*' Such action by the wife is punishable as adultery.

And it is so, not only in the case of the wife, but also of her accomplice – that is to say, the man who has furnished the seminal fluid (art. 338) – at least if he gave it while knowing fully that it was for the artificial insemination of a married woman.

As the penal legislation concerning adultery must be applied here, this matter cannot be waived by the consent of the husband of the fecundated wife. The disturbance caused to the social order by the establishing of a false paternity remains in spite of the husband's complicity. But the import of this regulation is diminished by the fact that the police cannot prosecute with sanctions adulterous women and their accomplices except on the complaint of the husband (art. 336 C. pen.). The prosecutors even demand that he should be the plaintiff, which he will be very reluctant to do if he has consented to the insemination.

There remains one final question, from the point of view of penal law: Do public descriptions of the processes of artificial insemination, and, eventually, propaganda in favour of these processes, constitute a moral outrage? The answer cannot be general and uniform. Everything depends on the form such description takes and the circumstances which accompany it. Provided it remains scientific and technical, and without any scandalous setting, the tribunals will find no offence in it.

2. The civil law

In the matter of civil law, artificial insemination can pose, on almost all points, the same questions as those arising from sexual relations. Thus, whether in the case of a husband or of a married woman, the fact of one spouse consenting in this matter in regard to a third party, gives the other the right to demand divorce, in accordance with the law now in use. For artificial insemination is equivalent to adultery properly so called, and would constitute, at any rate in the eyes of jurisprudence, a serious injury to the other spouse. It involves a definite failure to respect the promise of exclusive giving of self which the latter has received from his or her partner in marriage. Similarly, the fact of securing by disloyal contrivance that a woman, and especially a minor, should submit to artificial insemination, fully exposes at least the contriver to an action for damages.

But it is above all the question of legal filiation which artificial fecundation raises, because the determination of paternity is not left by French law to the free assessment of a judge resting on some proof or other. This proof is minutely and imperatively regulated by the law, which prefers some errors and voluntary omissions to what it considers as scandals dangerous to the legal constitution of the family.

But in this point of view, an important distinction must be made according to whether the woman artificially inseminated is or is not married.

If we suppose her to be single at the time of conception, the paternity of the donor of the seminal fluid is a simple natural paternity. The most normal proof results from the legal recognition of the child, which must be effected before a civil officer of state or a notary. It is but exceptionally that the natural paternity can be juridically proved if he does not wish to recognise it. The cases in which the juridical request for paternity is admitted are definitely numbered by art. 340 C. civ. But two of them: violent seduction and notorious concubinage are outside the orbit of artificial insemination. On the contrary, cases of rape, when there is written and unequivocal admission of paternity by a man, or finally, the case where he has voluntarily contributed to the upkeep and education of the child, can be equally applied to artificial insemination as to normal fecundation.

It must be noticed, however, that even in these hypotheses, artificial insemination does not give an absolutely certain paternity. In particular, the exceptions of art. 340 must be here applied, in seeking to establish paternity. If during the period between the 180th and the 300th day preceding the birth, the woman is proved to have had sexual relations with another man; or if her conduct during that period has been of a notorious kind, the request for paternity must remain unacceptable. It will be equally unacceptable where adulterous paternity is regarded as possible.

The conditions of proof are more rigid still if the insemination has been practised on a married woman. And they will apply in every case in which the mother of the child has been married at any time during the period from the 180th to the 300th day preceding the birth. In such a case, the woman's child is regarded as having the husband as father; and the husband, whose marriage is an act of confidence in the woman, continues to regard himself as the father, though insemination of this woman by a third party is certain and well-established. This is the ruling of art. 312 of the Civil Code.

It is only in altogether exceptional cases that the husband is allowed to disavow the child; these rules will hold good for a case of artificial insemination as well as for a case of natural fecundation. First of all, there is the case of physical impossibility of cohabitation, either by reason of separation or because of physical impotence in the husband. Then there is the case in which the wife has been guilty of dissimulation, either by concealing her pregnancy from her husband or by alleging an unknown mother on the child's birth certificate. Finally, there is the hypothesis that the child could have been conceived in the course of a separation or a divorce process. Apart from these exceptional circumstances, the fact of the husband's having allowed his wife to be artificially inseminated implies for him not only an adoption of the child, but also the obligation to impose the child on his whole family as though he had been the child of his flesh.

It will be noticed, moreover, that the technique of artificial insemination can prevent a husband's demand for the disavowal of his wife's child from being considered as definitive, when that demand is based on separation or on his impotence. But in the case where a wife claims to have been inseminated artificially with the semen of her husband, the onus of proof must rest with her in reply to an action of disavowal brought against her child.

The action of artificial insemination demands a preparation and a technique which would scarcely give it the intimate and secret character of coitus. The proof is, therefore, in certain cases, very easy. But the Code does nothing to underline that facility. And this omission, answering originally to simple ignorance on the part of the legislator, ought to be systematically maintained to-day, because the legal respect for the secrecy of the sexual act is closely connected with the safeguarding of decency and of human dignity.

R. SAVATIER
*Professeur à la Faculté de Droit de
l'Université de Poitiers*

PSYCHOLOGICAL AND MORAL
INCIDENCES

The invention of a procedure such as artificial insemination has the effect of posing to human liberty, in certain circumstances, a possibility outside the range of life such as it has been not only lived, but imagined, up to our own day. The ethical problem for the conscience is to know whether it is lawful or not, in certain circumstances, to make use of the means thus made available. But reflection immediately shows that this question which appears simple hides another infinitely more difficult one: that of knowing if, in introducing here the categories of the permitted and the forbidden, we do not still remain unduly within the ethico-social framework which this possibility actually leaves behind. From this point of view, it is somewhat absurd to condemn the practice of artificial insemination in the name of a system of rules of which this practice implies fundamentally, if not the decline, at least the essential irrelevance.

It is as well here to be as concrete as possible, and consider a couple who find that it is impossible for them to have children because of some organic deficiency or of a defect, which may be hidden, in the case of one of the parties. The husband or the wife lament this compulsory sterility. The doctor, when consulted, shows them the possibility which artificial insemination offers as a remedy for their sorrow. He is in a position to assure them that the donor has undergone every desirable examination, that he enjoys perfect health, that his ancestors are known and that no blemish has been found among them. He points out to them that medically the proposed operation is no different in any essential characteristic from a blood-transfusion of which no one to-day would think of questioning the legitimacy, and which is even, in many cases, the only way of saving the injured from imminent death. There is, however, a good chance that the doctor will meet with opposition on the part of the couple, due to a repugnance of which, it is true, they themselves are not able clearly to formulate the motives. The doctor will not hesitate, of course, to attribute this to rooted prejudices. 'Why,' he will doubtless say, "do you not consider the possibility which is here very simply offered to you, and think of it as what might be called a kind of generalised horticulture? After all, it is merely a question of using a semen put at her disposal.' Let us suppose now that the couple, while not seeing clearly what arguments they can oppose to those of the doctor, are unable to overcome this strange moral repugnance, and that they ask a philosopher friend if he thinks that this trouble, this inquietude is without significance and if he would advise them to ignore it. If, as unfortunately is very rare, the philosopher has a sense of the concrete, it would seem that his reflection on the matter should take this form: first of all, he will think, it is necessary to re-establish a certain context, from which the doctor would have the couple to turn away. This semen is human; that is to say, it has not been simply found, nor has it been procured, as some product or other is obtained, by means of mechanical operations on raw material. Nor can it be said that this semen is comparable with a secretion, since the active consent of the donor was necessary. It may be urged that this consent is equally necessary in the case of blood transfusion. But there is a clear difference between the act of allowing blood to be drawn off for a determined purpose, and the act of provoking an emission of sperm by masturbation. It will then be further objected that masturbation practised in such circumstances ceases to be an unlawful act, that it receives here, if not an ethical, at least a sociological justification. But why cannot it be seen that we are here on the verge of the grotesque and the odious? Is it not the rôle of philosophic reflection to uncover the implications of the uneasiness felt by those who consult the philosopher? Here as always, the affective trouble presents a semeiological value, and it is dishonest to pretend to set it aside as if it were a simple mechanical and insignificant reaction.

Let us consider more clearly the case of the donor from whom the doctor would divert our attention. Either he contents himself with a lucrative post, which, if it is not carried out without fatigue, does not involve any work – inasmuch as the community is bound to assure him his keep, if this professional begetter is to remain in its service; and in this case it must be said quite simply that we have here an onanistic prostitute. Or we must suppose that this donor acts from a philanthropic motive, and that he means to serve humanity by giving his semen. But in this second case, it is the grotesque note which resounds like the boom of a bassoon, and it is of the nature of this grotesque that it requires explanation. Is there not something contradictory in behaving as a stallion, as a purely productive animal, while thereby regarding oneself as a benefactor of humanity? Why, during some official ceremony, is not a medal presented for the record in humanitarian masturbation?

The activity of the donor appears, therefore, as fundamentally equivocal or hybrid: it is not known and it cannot be known in what measure it is the achievement of the man or the achievement of the animal. But how can we forget that when a man behaves *like an animal*, he falls *far below the animal*.

Nevertheless, the doctor will probably interrupt the philosopher at this point and, in a great state of agitation, will observe that the error consists in looking at the whole affair in the perspective of the donor. The latter, as human, he will say, must not be taken into account. It is not for the woman, into whom the semen is injected, to question in any way his moral quality. The matter differs entirely from that implied in her committing adultery with a despicable creature, since she will not have seen this man who is the donor, and she will have had no personal relations with him. Does not scientific progress, the doctor will perhaps suggest, lie in the fact that technical skill comes to depersonalise an operation which secular prejudices lead us to consider always by referring it to the individuals concerned?

Artificial insemination would indeed point the way to a much greater achievement, by making it ultimately conceivable that gestation may be possible in an artificial uterus. If that day comes, it will no longer be possible to speak of Paul as the son of James and of Susan; in the final analysis, there will be no longer any reason for the entities which these Christian names are meant to designate.

But let us set aside these extreme possibilities, and simply ask ourselves, if, in the case with which we are concerned, this depersonalisation is purely fictitious. In spite of all this reasoning, there is no getting away from the fact that the woman must bear within her for nine months this seed whose origin she is so incessantly told to ignore. Supposing that the gestation presents here the psychological characteristics of a parthenogenesis – which is at least a doubtful supposition – it will remain to enquire if this parthenogenesis itself does not imply destructive possibilities for the union of husband and wife.

Here again an attempt may be made to evade the difficulty by alleging that the husband, though non-existent here on the physical plane, is nevertheless associated with the operation. He consents to it, and he meets its expenses. He is thus associated with it, and he participates in his wife's eager hope. But here again, we are visibly faced with the absurd, the burlesque. It will, of course, be admitted that the husband cannot possibly be jealous of the anonymous donor, that he will confine himself to abstract envy of his stallion qualities. But it is quite impossible that this absence of jealousy will go the length of being completely unconscious of the other's existence. What will be his reaction in relation to this other person who, after all, has been substituted for himself and has done what he himself could not? Whatever this reaction may be – and it can be pretty undefined – it would be bad faith to pretend that it is negligible in itself. Psychologically it is almost unthinkable that the intervention in question would seem to the husband's mind to be a simple operation which is to be performed for its own sake and without any reference to the personality of the operator. It must be agreed, as in the natural order of things, that the wife cannot fail to react psychologically to this reaction which is perhaps unavowed but which is inevitably suspected. In these conditions, the reciprocal situation of the couple cannot but be subtly modified in a manner which, however, cannot be estimated at all, because it is impossible for human beings to imagine in advance how they will feel in such a case. At any rate, the almost monstrous inequality between the rôle of the husband – which dwindled to a vague consent, tinged, perhaps, with irritation and rancour – and the decisive rôle of the wife, cannot fail to cause a disturbing disequilibrium in the home, especially when the child has arrived – the child of the unknown father. It is true that on this point, the situation analysed is not absolutely different from that of a widow or a divorced woman with a child, who makes a second marriage with a man incapable of making her conceive. Nevertheless, this assimilation which appears legitimate in the abstract does not perhaps correspond to the concrete conditions of experience. Indeed, in the case of second marriage, there is no reason why the husband should feel any sort of 'bad sexual conscience,' which threatens, on the other hand, to wreak havoc in the home which seeks artificial insemination as the remedy for sterility.

In the final analysis, the philosopher will be bound to reveal an illusion or error under which the doctor who discusses the matter with him is labouring, and which vitiates all argumentation. To assimilate insemination with transfusion is to lose sight of the specific character of the sperm as such; it carries a man's history, it is the real bearer of it, and this in conditions which, to tell the truth, evade all distinct analysis and consequently all conjecture. It can be said, I think, that in a world such as ours, where the personal and historical factor keeps a primary place, the difficulties I have emphasized ought probably to be judged insurmountable; but inversely, those same difficulties would tend to disappear in a world which would be, if I may coin the word, 'anonymised,' where the individual would be less and less considered and appreciated in his unicity, being more and more treated as a simple specimen labelled and numbered. But it must be said, on the other hand, that to have recourse to processes such as artificial insemination is in fact to proceed as though this 'anonymised' world were already ours, and, which is more serious still, to contribute actively towards preparing the way for its coming. This last point is capital, and I must insist on it here.

Does not the illusion consist, indeed, in believing that one can remain in a system of determined values, while one has recourse at the same time to processes which suppose the negation of these same values? I may add that the term *process* is inadequate here, or more exactly, that its use implies already the degradation which I am envisaging. Consider in effect: is there not something which spontaneously shocks us in saying that such and such a process is employed to have a child? Can human love, considered even at its most carnal, be assimilated in any fashion whatsoever to a *process*? Here an analysis bearing on the notion of metaphysical essence would certainly be required. Think what is implied in the traditional and, moreover, mysterious idea of the *giving of self*. A woman gives herself to a man; and a relation, itself mysterious I admit, has always been recognised, at least until our day, to establish itself for the conscience of the partners in marriage, between this giving and the birth of the being in whom this giving seems to become incarnate. On the contrary, all this is mechanised and debased if the union is considered simply as a means, exterior to being, of realising a certain end. It is evident that this degradation is possible, that it can be logically visualised without any contradiction – visualised and realised. It is possible exactly in the way that prostitution is possible. It would even be of the greatest importance to ask ourselves in what sense it is correct to say that the possibility is implied in our own situation, but also to show how this situation changes from the moment such possibility is actualised.

Fundamentally, we here find ourselves in the presence of a phenomenon of alienation which tends manifestly to become general under our eyes. Man tends to consider his own essence and the constitutive relations of his own being, from the starting-point and on the principles of a dehumanised nature. It will not be contested that this would be legitimate and even necessary up to a certain point – but on the express condition that a limit is maintained and respected; if, on the contrary, such limit is crossed, man enters on a way which can lead only to the absolute or systematic desecration of life and of the values of which it is the focus. In a world where practices such as artificial insemination would be commonly accepted, it is hard to see how the dissociation of love and pleasure can fail to tend towards becoming the rule. But the consequences of such dissociation are easy to imagine. Would not a woman whose husband is weak and puny be very naturally tempted to give herself the luxury of having recourse to a donor of outstanding beauty and virility? In other words, certain accepted beliefs of yesterday would inevitably be called in question. Here as everywhere in this domain, the narrow breach of a tolerated exception has a tendency to enlarge itself until it causes the whole structure to topple, though it was the original intention of the exception-maker that the structure should be respected. In short, it is to be recognised that where something sacred must be preserved, it is inevitable that such rigid negative additions as 'in no circumstances' or 'under no pretext' should find place in the formulations. In the secular order, these negative formulations should not have the freedom of the city of human conduct, since everything there is a question of particular cases. And that is precisely what can never be said of sacred things, because here the commandments are absolute.

But it does definitely seem that we have come to a moment in history when the sense of absolute prohibitions and commands, of any kind whatsoever, is practically lost. It is besides only natural that the atheist should have lost this sense. It is indeed amazing, in their turn, to see believers allowing themselves to be drawn on to that slope, without their ceasing however to hold on to their own particular form of belief; and it is against this sort of interior defection that a group such as this one, must, in my opinion, vigorously react.

GABRIEL MARCEL

ARTIFICIAL INSEMINATION
IN ENGLAND

At a time when France, because of total war, was cut off from all relations with the Anglo-Saxon world, Great Britain was tightening more and more, as month followed month, her links with the United States. All advances in surgical or medical technique passed very rapidly from one country to the other by reason of their alliance in war. Now, the years 1940 to 1945 saw a development and expansion of the processes of artificial insemination in the United States. In 1941, Seymour and Kernet could base their conclusions on 9,580 cases of artificial insemination. There were, in addition, many communications which, from all parts, brought the result of this process, as newly used on human beings, to the notice of the principal American medical reviews. English doctors were thus led to study for themselves this question which was causing real enthusiasm among some of their transatlantic colleagues.

Leaving aside the technical aspect with which Dr. Palmer dealt at the beginning of these lectures, we wish to give a brief objective sketch of the psychological and ethical problems which presented themselves then to the English medical world, and of some reactions of public opinion.

One of the first questions to be answered was: To what cases must insemination with a donor be reserved? Must it be reserved only to the case of sterility of the husband? The majority of English 'inseminators' adopt this rule, but there is a tendency which makes a show of putting this process at the service of eugenic theories.

In an article[1] which was noted by the most observant by reason of its fulness and the importance of its conclusions, three specialists described two cases in which they believed that artificial insemination by a donor should take the place of

1. Artificial Insemination by Mary Barton, First assistant, Fertility clinic, Royal Free Assistant, Kenneth Walker, genito-urinary surgeon, Royal London Hospital, and B. P. Wiesner, Consulting Biologist, Royal Northern Hospital, in British Medical Journal, Jan. 13th, 1945, p. 40 et seq.

insemination by the husband: the first case concerns deafness transmitted for three generations in the husband's family; the second concerns the case where the existence of a transmittable nervous disease has been diagnosed.

But the most delicate point for these 'eugenists' was that of the choice and selection of donors. At first, some doctors proposed in the first place the husband's brother because of the geno-typical resemblance. Experience, however, quickly weakened this choice; it was incompatible with the discretion judged to be necessary, and it contributed to stir up discontent between husband and wife. In fact, there is general accord that the parents should never know the identity of the donor. Many examples have shown that the donor and the woman fecundated are too deeply interested in the procreation to remain insensible to the paternal filiation of the child. The English 'inseminators' now jealously preserve anonymity to the extent that the donor is never described to the sterile couple except in the vaguest terms which exclude all identification.

The discussion then turns on the 'ideal' type of donor: shall he be of the athletic type, or an intellectual endowed with such and such a quality? The selected donor – we had almost written 'prime stallion' – seems, according to the notes, to require the following characteristics: above-normal intelligence, perfect health, age from 35 to 40, proved social qualities, the father of two legitimate children, Rh negative blood group identical with that of one of the spouses. The complexus of qualities limits the number of donors, and English doctors admit the difficulty of obtaining them. It is true that a single donor, if he consented to two 'donations' per week, would render possible 400 insemi-nations weekly (0.01 c.c. of semen being sufficient for each fecundation). And as the authors of these researches often do not hesitate to push their statistics to extreme limits, they have gravely calculated that a single donor could become in a year the father of about 20,000 children, if all the interventions were successful.

It is then that a new difficulty crops up for the 'eugenists.' Does it not follow that, in a few years, marriage between children of the same father will grow to alarming proportions, and this in the most complete ignorance of their real paternal connections? To obviate such an inconvenience for the future of the race, it is agreed to limit the activity of each donor to 100 pregnancies resulting in birth. Beyond that figure, the donor must not be used.

Finally, to relieve the practitioner from this delicate matter of seeking a possible donor, and to procure for him semen in conformity with the required conditions, ought not certain laboratories or 'banks' to be set up? In an exposition to the Medico-Legal Society of England,[1] Robert Forbes envisages guarantees of all kinds which he considers, in the present state of knowledge, to be necessary for obtaining these donors.

In this same lecture, the legal aspect of artificial insemination was fully commented on. Does English law admit fecundation with an outside 'donor'? If English law, like French law, did not foresee a case of this kind, at least jurisprudence seems to be able to cast some light on it. There exists, for example, a decision of the Supreme Court of Ontario in 1921 (the Orford case) which upheld the charge of adultery against a woman who was artificially inseminated in England at a time when her husband resided at Toronto. In such cases, the child is declared illegitimate and the donor, if he is known, can be proceeded against as an accomplice. In another case – the Russell case – Lord Linlay declared that fecundation by a donor can be legally considered adultery.

It can be appreciated, therefore, that the Anglo-Saxon would earnestly endeavour, as Dr. Palmer points out at the end of his exposition, to anticipate by a wealth of written precautions any danger, proximate or remote, that might arise for those who take part in artificial insemination, such precautions aiming at providing legal protection. In the present condition of English legislation, it is difficult, as admitted by those who study the juridical aspect of the problem, to find the means of assuring a complete defence of the doctor. But up to now, English justice has been called upon only on the occasion of some very rare complaints.

1. The Medico-Legal aspects of artificial insemination, by Robert Forbes, in the Medico-Legal and Criminological Review, July-September, 1944, p. 138 et seq.

The meeting of the Medico-Legal Society of England, to which we have referred above, ends however with a condemnation of artificial insemination, on the legal and the moral plane, by the President of the Society itself, Mr. Roland Burrows. He was merely echoing an important body of opinion in the medical world.

Dr. Leonard J. Parsons, a well-known pediatrist, writes in the *British Medical Journal* –

'Many of our correspondents appear to think that the Church and especially the Roman Catholic Church, ought to have no say in this matter; but questions which concern personal conduct, the sanctity of the home, and the situation of married people, are the vital concern of the Church. However, if the Church said nothing on this matter, it seems abundantly clear that those who call themselves Christians and profess that faith, ought to have no part in the practice of extra-marital insemination. It throws a strange light on eugenic arguments, to see eugenists labouring to bring about a state of society in which no one can be sure any longer of his own origin or the origin of his neighbour. It is the Catholics who now plead that the child should be at least sure of its own father.... This question scarcely admits of discussion in the press, but it would be as well that a Catholic couple who are contemplating a remedy for sterility should first consult a priest before going further.'

The English custom of opening the newspaper columns to letters from subscribers and readers gives us an opportunity to assess the reaction of the public itself. The reasons for and against are alternately put forward. Some see in insemination a means by which England can meet her birth crisis, and the solution for augmenting by emigration the population of certain dominions such as Australia. Others protest by showing the immoral aspect of such medical practice. One of them, M. R. Walshe, for example, writes –

'If there is no objection to extra-marital insemination, the question can certainly be pressed much further, with an equal freedom of conscience. There must be celibate women whose lives could be transformed by maternity. Why not put this 'Service' to their profit?

'There are also thousands of married men overseas, separated from their wives. Would not these men desire to give a sort of power of attorney to the Inseminator to enable his donors and his syringe to act in their place? If we once begin, where are we to draw the line? And why should we not really search out all the possibilities of this new technique? A syringe has no morality and can entail no moral sanction. Why this concern with 'sentiment,' which causes M. K. Walker to remark a little naively that a little of what you fancy does you good.

'When such technical knowledge falls into the hands of men who admit only utilitarian morality without metaphysical foundation, they are a constant menace both to intellectual and to moral values. This becomes abundantly clear when we look about us in a world where man is torn and tormented by the results of technical knowledge which he is unable to control because he lacks both wisdom and the appreciation of values necessary to his doing so. The doctor, to-day, is on the point of being contaminated by this evil; and every doctor who has at heart the traditions of medicine as those of a human profession, ought to feel himself called upon to protest in no uncertain terms.'

Other English readers voice the problem of the maternal sentiment of the woman who undergoes insemination by a donor –

'What kind of woman asks for artificial insemination?' asks one of them. 'If the desire of a childless wife cannot be satisfied by the adoption of a child who suits her, is she not better without a child? Does not every inseminated woman choose between her love and the simple satisfaction of being no longer a sterile woman in the eyes of the world?'

On the whole, English opinion seems to be opposed to this American wave of artificial insemination. This practice, far from being accepted with enthusiasm, is actually the object of impassioned discussion; in effect, it is too offensive to a certain human and Christian sense in the English spirit. The final impression which our enquiries yield can be definitely summarised in the following answer –

'We speak, I am sure, for many who have remained silent…

For my part, the matter is urgent and I must speak. Our children will blame us for having remained silent in face of a process which is incontestably not English... Our answer must be an emphatic 'No!' '

PÈRE CH. LARÈRE
Aumonier-Directeur de la Conférence Laënnec

ARTIFICIAL INSEMINATION AND THE MORAL LAW

PRELIMINARY NOTE: THE DOCTOR AND THE THEOLOGIAN

Each time the theologian has occasion to treat with the specialised technician in a particular branch of research or of scientific
practice, concerning a particular problem, they must begin,
before reaching the subject under debate at that moment, by
considering matters of higher import so that they may establish
a common ground of general principles acceptable to both.

We may, perhaps, attempt an exposition of this initial preparation with the amplitude it deserves. We cannot do so to-day;
but we may be allowed at least a few brief remarks on the subject.

Technical knowledge, philosophy, theology, apart from their
methods, engender attitudes of mind which tend to ignore one
another and thus end by opposing one another; because the
devotees of each branch are concerned exclusively with the
matter of their own work and stubbornly refuse to stray from
their chosen path. The financier, the economist, the politician
claim boldly that they can build the earthly city by obeying
exclusively the laws of the science to which they have given their
energies. They regard in a hostile manner the intruder who
comes, in the name of some principles or other announced with
an assurance of one untroubled by the least doubt that *he* holds
the truth, to meddle with matters about which he knows nothing
and which he has not even take the trouble to study. Let such
intruder stay, therefore, in his own domain, in his seminary or
his sacristy, let him draw up rules for private living, for the
problems of the personal conscience; technical matters are not
subject to his surveillance, his interdicts, his imperative commands; technical matters have their own requirements, and let
those who seek to conform to such requirements be left in peace.

The same holds good for the doctor. Eager to care for his
patient and to attempt his cure, he sees only the concrete case,
the painful state of affairs he is called on to remedy. His province

is to respond to that appeal for help and to do all in his power to suppress the cause of the evil and the sorrow. And if someone comes to him and says: 'To save the mother who comes for assistance to you, you are about to kill an innocent child; that is a crime, and you have no right to do it, any more than you have the right to hasten the death of the old man, unquestionably doomed and racked with suffering,' he will be angry, or he will merely shrug his shoulders. Let the theologian give battle, if he so wishes, on the plane of the abstract, with concepts, with principles already worked out; for his part, the doctor is at grips with problems of real life, and must be excused from such conceptual warfare in the best interests of his patients and allowed to act in accordance with his knowledge and his conscience.

If we wish to summarise this opposition between technical knowledge, on the one hand, and philosophy and theology on the other, we can say that it bears chiefly on three points. Firstly, while the specialist looks only to one part of reality – and deliberately does so, because such limitation is the condition of his success; since, for him, man is considered merely from the viewpoint of one of his functions, one of his activities, one of his states, neither the philosopher nor the theologian can hold that either must confine himself to such limitations to judge a human action correctly. One point of view only is admissible for the philosopher or the theologian: that of the totality. They do not reject analysis; on the contrary, indeed, they wish it to be as detailed and as perfect as the power of intellect and the scope of instruments can make it. But when the moment comes to judge of good and evil, of what should or should not be done, they find that they cannot accept conditions which limit them exclusively to the viewpoint of a particular activity, a function considered alone. Let us consider the example of sexuality. Man is a sexed being: his whole comportment, his whole person are marked by this disposition of his nature; it would be absurd as well as ineffectual to attempt to deal with the virtue of chastity without knowing in what consists the instinctive and sentimental forces over which it must rule. But this would not be a less serious failure of method than to give a judgment on a sexual act while deciding to ignore systematically the other components of human nature, and to decide the value of such an act solely, for example, by eugenic consequences.

The theologian treats of the whole man, in the complexity of his tendencies, in the diversity of his elements. Such a position is certainly more difficult than the specialised one. But surely it is the only one which is loyal and which respects reality in its fullness.

One of Aldous Huxley's characters, in *Point Counterpoint*, expressed perfectly the data of the problem: 'To be a complete, balanced man is a difficult undertaking.... Nobody's asking you to be anything but a man. A man, mind you. Not an angel or a devil. A man's a creature on a tight-rope, walking delicately, equilibrated, with mind and consciousness and spirit at one end of his balancing pole and body and instinct and all that's unconscious and earthy and mysterious at the other. Balanced. Which is damnably difficult.' (Chatto & Windus, 1928. P. 560.)

In fact, it is the opposition we have placed here in the second place, which would command the first. The need for the totality of which we speak is principally a *hierarchical* requirement. In our estimation of things, certain values must necessarily imply such a hierarchy. In fact, if we ought never to forget that man is a corporal and social being; that physiology involves his whole personality even to its highest functions; that he is carnal, even in his love of God, as St. Augustine remarked; that he is also a being caught up in an almost infinite web of social relations; that he is debtor to the past as well as to the present, and to economics as well as to politics – still less should we forget his essential quality, that which makes him a man, his *spirit*. Of course, this element must not be considered in isolation from the elements which we have just enumerated; it is united to them in a vital blending, but it has the right to first place in that complex whole. It is indispensably necessary, in forming a judgment on a human action, to take into account, always and above all, the requirements of the spirit.

Biologists have drawn up for us a magnificent description of the evolution of life, and perhaps the believers have not gazed with sufficient admiration on those splendours which are revealed only to patient seekers. But enthralling as these discoveries are, they concern only the less perfect form of life; beyond that form and constituting new orders of being, there are the life of the intellect, the moral life, and the religious life. Actions such as that of the scientist in putting his eye to the microscope, or the widow's mite singled out by Christ for the admiration of His disciples, seem out of proportion to the natural forces which they use. It is the primacy of the spiritual in the human complex that the theologian must recall to those who might be tempted to forget it. And which of us has not encountered that temptation, especially in our times when the human person is menaced from all sides by the organised votaries of technical procedures? Faced with certain interdictions of the moral law, it is for technicians to call on all the resources of their inventiveness to discover the procedure which does not violate the requirements of the spirit. Is this really impossible?

Finally, the technician is often hurt by the affirmation of the *absolute character* of the moral law: the imperative *yes* and the imperative *no*. That law seems inhuman, because it takes no account of particular situations. Surely each has his own destiny? Inhuman, too, because it attaches importance to actions which are often regarded of little importance by their authors. Let us understand from whence comes this intransigent character of the moral law – that character which constitutes its worth. We have within us a mysterious faculty of appreciation which weighs our actions and determines their value, judging some to be praiseworthy, some mediocre, while some are reprehensible. The rule which guides this faculty in its judgment is not that of immediate convenience or tangible result. The personal interest of the man whose country demands of him that he should risk his life, is certainly not to have himself killed. What pronounces a judgment of value on an action is the mind, and in doing so it takes as its rule: an action is good which, in all the given circumstances, respects spiritual values; on the contrary, it is bad if it attacks them or disturbs the hierarchy of which we have spoken above and which gives the first place to the spiritual side of our nature. One would never place on the same level benevolence and cruelty, debauchery and industry. And, be it noted, this judgment which is exercised on our actions does not stem from an exterior authority; it arises from the very requirements of our nature, taken in its complexity and its totality. This is why the moral law is not a code of juridical prescriptions which must be blindly obeyed because they are the dictates of an arbitrary will; the moral law is stamped on our nature and expresses that to which we ought to aspire for the full realisation of our nature.

We say that the decisions of the moral law are not dictated by immediate convenience. But this must not be misunderstood. If the moral law imposes sacrifice, if it says *no* to one part of our being, is it a law of liberty and of life. The reign of the spirit which it seeks to establish in the individual and by consequence in society, is a condition of happiness and of progress.

Are the sacrifices which it in effect demands proportionate to the havoc engendered by a wholesale violation of the law?

This law written in man's nature forbids, for example, in all circumstances the direct and voluntary killing of the innocent. It can happen that, in some very rare cases, which it is the province of medical science to reduce still more by its progress, obedience to this imperative command results in the loss of two human lives instead of one; for with the death of the child, it involves also the death, sorrowfully accepted but not willed, of the pregnant mother. But are we to forget the *six hundred thousand* sacrificed by abortion each year in France?

It may be answered, perhaps, that this is to join two facts that have no connection with each other. Is tolerance of therapeutic abortion, when serious doctors judge it indispensable, to be equated with the practices of illegal abortionists and of unscrupulous doctors? Happily, no. But once an exception is admitted, the principle will crumble entirely, little by little. Should abortion be permitted in one of those tragic cases to which we have alluded above, when there is a necessary choice of either the life of the mother or the life of the child? And then, why be less tolerant to the young girl who is the victim of a drunken brute? Must she endure a pregnancy for which she was in no manner responsible? Again, here is a woman whose husband has been absent for some months; she had yielded to weakness and is carrying an adulterous child; would it not be better to save the peace of that family by destroying the result of her lapse? The reasons? These will certainly be forthcoming to create an imperative necessity in each particular case.

It is strange that the soldier should be commanded to stay at his post, cost what it may; that desertion in face of the enemy is ordinarily punished by death; and yet that it is not understood that the moral law also can demand terrible sacrifices to safeguard values – values which transcend the interests of a terrestrial city.

But, it may be urged – and this is also used as an answer to the preceding objection – if the moral law expresses merely the requirements of our inseparably corporal and spiritual nature, why not let each person listen to that law as it speaks in himself? Surely, in this matter, every man is his own proper guide and sole judge? Undoubtedly we must follow the dictates of our conscience, which are supreme for each of us; but conscience is not that blind instinct of which Jean-Jacques Rousseau speaks. It is nothing other than the mind exercising itself in the domain of morals. Now, the mind can be cultivated, and such cultivation is even necessary if it is to reach its point of full maturity. In this sphere, as in every other, man is a debtor to his environment. In spite of the fact that each of us has a particular temperament, that each is caught up in a destiny and a drama which are personal to each – nevertheless, nature is fundamentally identical in all of us, in all its aspects. This is the reason why a common conscience exists, through the experience of centuries, which guides and clarifies individual consciences. Accord is reached gradually on the principal points of moral life.

Moreover, since men live in society, it is indispensable that their relations should be ruled by custom or written laws, and this imposes a restraint on the individual. His conscience is not violated, but, under penalty of sanctions, he is obliged to submit to certain general rules in his exterior actions. Abortion may be forbidden; robbery and assassination ordinarily are forbidden. Even if his conscience were to tell him that in a given case he would commit no fault by killing one of his fellow men; even if it told him that such an act would be meritorious, he risks incurring the chastisement provided by the code for such infractions, if he does so. It must therefore be clearly understood that the individual is not left to himself in the government of his life and that he is not entirely free to do as he pleases, without incurring some evil thereby.

This example of the relations of the members of the earthly city with each other leads us to the discussion of the case which most often proves difficult, that of the Catholic Church. Her pretensions seem exorbitant, unacceptable. It is with her in mind, especially, that statements like this are made: 'My conscience suffices for me; I have no need that anyone should come to teach me what I should do.' When there is question of artificial birth-control methods, of masturbation, of so-called therapeutic abortion…, the Catholic Church answers in all such cases: 'This is not permitted; this is *never* permitted.' By what right does she teach with such authority, in a manner so absolute? By what right does she claim total obedience? She is the visible society of those who believe that Christ is the envoy and the Son of God; and is it not normal that in her should be found a hierarchy – not of personal distinction, but, on the contrary, forming as it were her soul – charged with ensuring the transmission to all ages of the evangelical message? Nothing must be lost of Christ's words, in order that all men may be able to draw life from them, even to the end of time.

The moral and religious ideal, which the Church has received as a deposit, comprises in the first place the doctrines of Christ: love of one's neighbour, worship of God, Father and Providence, the need for purity, etc.…, but it is necessary that the precepts of the natural law should be found there too, as the indispensable foundations. Grace elevates nature, but does so by first of all aiding nature to accomplish and realise its own secret aspirations. That is why these aspirations, these laws inscribed in the nature of man, but not with an immediate, absolute evidence, are sought out by the Church; her philosophers, her theologians, discuss them, and sometimes discuss them for a long time, before an answer can be clearly formulated; but once that solution is reached, the authority of the Church intervenes, for it is her rôle to say: it is thus, and there can no longer be any doubt. And thus, on a law which is clearly expressed for all time, she cannot give way, nor return to the attitude of indecision and research; for she is among men as the guardian of moral and religious values. To admit, therefore, an exception would be equivalent in reality to admitting that a valid law of life can break down at some point.

Such an admission would be a betrayal of her mission by the Church even towards those who claim dispensation because they are in an awkward situation, because this would be to allow them to settle down into mediocrity, into irregularity; it would also be a betrayal of those who wish to conform to the law, because in order to lure man to the heights, it is necessary to show him the demands of the absolute. Finally, such a betrayal, fraught with consequences for its own epoch, would be also heavy with consequences for the future, because, as we have said, the message must be faithfully transmitted to future generations, that they may find therein the leaven of life.

When the Church thus promulgates these rules, she addresses herself directly, it is true, only to the faithful; but she nevertheless aims at outlining clearly the duties which bind the consciences of all men. For every man, whether he be a Christian or not, abortion is a crime.

However, we candidly recognise that to perceive the full import of the Church's teaching, even on the natural law, we must have complete faith and confidence in the Church herself as the instrument of God in the world. For though it is true that, theoretically, the human mind left to itself can discover truth, it is none the less certain that, in actual fact, too many influences, especially emotional influences, shackle our reason and prevent it from reaching the limits of its field. It is perhaps necessary, if we are to see all that is good and evil in the heart of man and thus discover the profound ordinances of his nature, that we should take a more elevated point of view. To understand what man is, perhaps it is necessary to remind ourselves of the end God has determined for us, of what He wishes to make of us, of our effective destiny. It is through the Christian revelation that we are enabled to know ourselves as men, just as it is through the grace of Christ that the disturbed balance of our nature is corrected and we are enabled to live a normal life, which, in spite of failures, remains faithful to our nature. The Church, therefore, is not a substitute for our conscience, but she points out to our conscience the duties of a man and of a Christian; she is our teacher. If one is inclined to complain, one should examine the ideas which she has sown in the world.

The Christian, if he is a man of good will and has not neglected to acquaint himself with the doctrine he professes, knows this mission of the Church and places his confidence in it, despite some obscurities which fall to his lot in common with his fellow men and some anguish and heart searchings which he shares with them. He knows that the Church which shares our weaknesses because she is ourselves, is nevertheless the custodian of life; and that her laws are those which, on a complete view, are most conducive to real progress.

ARTIFICIAL INSEMINATION AND
THE MORAL LAW

The problem posed by artificial insemination is but a particular case of a general problem which can be stated thus: In what measure has man the right, by means of his technical skill, to modify the body he has from nature, to suppress or to correct its activities?

Man is alive at all only because he has invented, that is to say, discovered a way to impose his will on natural forces and to use them for his purposes. Infra-human nature has become, as it were, malleable in his hands; he can control and fashion it to his needs. This is merely the formulation of a profound law. Nature is given to man in order that he may draw therefrom the nourishment of body and soul, and find therein the link which binds him to his fellow men. Nature is his; in using it, he is merely exercising his rights.

But since by his body he forms a physical and biological part of the universe, man is led on to attempt the application to himself of the technical skill he exercises on things. These attempts and these results, supposing that there are any results, raise no moral problem or even the least difficulty for those who regard utility or immediate results as the only criterion of human action. But for those who regard man as being above the rest of earthly things, who recognise that his nature cannot be reduced merely to physical and biological elements, but presents a complex union of matter and spirit – the answer is not so simple. Man has not the rights over himself that he has over things, which are his to mould according to his desires; for he is not his own master, he has merely a right of use over himself dependent on a will other than his own, that of his Creator. There is certainly nothing wrong with saying this. But this juridical language has the disadvantage of presenting the moral law too exclusively in a juridical form, that is to say, in its most superficial aspect. The dependence of man is a dependence of finality. Since his end is to establish in himself the reign of the spirit and of charity, he can do so only by submitting himself to the plan itself which is written in his nature and which expresses his likeness to God. Seen in this perspective, the human body takes on, as the instrument of the soul, a value which lifts it above the level of a mere animal body, and we recognise in its activities a destiny and a mode which cannot be arbitrarily modified.

Such being the case, we cannot raise an objection, in the name of the moral law, when the doctor or the surgeon attempts to rectify bodily deficiencies, either congenital or the results of illness, because such interventions help nature; they give to nature, as best they can, the use of its organs and functions. And even when, to safeguard physical life or to permit its free exercise, it is found necessary to sacrifice a part of the body, the general good of the individual takes precedence of the good of any component parts. Nevertheless, recourse to this principle is valid only when realities of the same order are compared, the body and one of its parts. No one has the right to deprive himself of a bodily function, by a directly destructive action, in the interests of the moral life. The Church has always condemned the conduct of those who would pretend, by castration, to suppress in themselves the cause of carnal desires.[1]

Man must establish in himself the progressive predominance of spiritual values; but he must do so only by acts which respect the laws of the human composite, because it is by directing the body to its proper ends that the spirit asserts its mastery, not by impairing its integrity.

Is the sacrifice of a part, permitted in the general interests of the whole body, equally lawful when there is question of sacrificing, through charity, part of one's body for the welfare of another person? For example, is it lawful to contribute to the cure of another by abandoning a part of one's self? Without becoming involved in the discussion of this controversial question, we say here that, kept within just limits, there is nothing *a priori* against such a sacrifice. It would be merely a particular case of a man's sacrificing something of his health, of his well-being, in the interests of his fellow man.

1. This is a very different case from that in which the sex glands are removed as a remedy for a condition of erotic alienation.

Such, in brief, are the general rules which regulate the application which man may make of technical knowledge to his own body.

But there is in human nature an activity, that of sex, which has a particular purpose and which has, in consequence, its particular laws. It is commonly held that the other functions of the body are ordained to the proper good of the body, while sex has for its end the perpetuity of the species. This, we think, is to characterise this function too extensively in terms of its biological value and thus risk the danger of being able to give but inadequate answers to certain difficulties. We underline the fact, first of all, that no other physical component stamps the individual as sex does. The castration of an infant causes profound disturbance in his personality, and when he reaches maturity, neither his body, nor his sensibility, nor his intelligence will be what they would have been had that mutilation not taken place. Need we also recall the repercussions of maternity on the psychology and even on the spirituality of the woman? In reality, the normal development of the genital apparatus and the influence of its hormones, act on the entire nature to dispose it to play its part in society, a part which is not limited to the transmission of life. When there is question, therefore, of whether man may apply his technical knowledge to the sex organs and their use, we must examine a complexity of ends to discover if this intervention is legitimate. For example, if we limit our view merely to the biological end of sex, it will be difficult, we think, to judge correctly of parthenogenesis or the culture of the human egg in an artificial way, if science progresses to a point where such attempts can be made with some chance of success. In this case, appeal must be made to the principles which regulate the constitution of the human family.

It will be necessary also to keep another consideration in mind. The technical intervention of which we speak can take two forms: in the one, the patient submits to an operation in the same way as all patients suffer the surgical knife; in the other, his co-operation is required. If moral difficulties arise in the first case (for example, if there is question of removing the ovaries in a woman), they will be discussed and decided according to the general rules we have dealt with in the preceding pages. In the second case, when the patient is required to act, such acts must be submitted to the laws which ought to govern all human action, unless we are to reject all morality or reduce it to a few vague formulae so imprecise as to have no binding force. Artificial insemination comes under this second category of interventions. To meet the moral problems raised by artificial insemination, therefore, we must have recourse to another set of principles – the principles of conjugal and family morality. We shall do so as briefly as possible, because there can be no question of giving to our discussion the technical form of a debate among theologians.

These problems arise for us in three distinct cases, even though the actions in question are often the same, or apparently the same, in each of these cases. First, there is the enquiry into the causes of the sterility of a couple, especially when this sterility seems traceable to a defect of the male organism. A second case is met with in which, for some reason, pregnancy can be obtained only by a supplementary and artificial intervention which introduces the seminal fluid into the interior of the uterine canal, the fluid having been supplied by the husband. Finally, there is the case where the husband proves incapable of all generative power, and it is decided to have recourse to a stranger, a 'donor.'

Each of these hypotheses calls for special treatment and for solutions which will vary according to the circumstances and to the techniques used.

1. When the doctor is consulted by the man and the woman whose union, in spite of normally exercised sexual activity, remains fruitless, he ought, in the first place, to seek out the cause of such sterility. It often happens that the attempts made to correct the possible deficiencies of the woman are of no avail, and it becomes necessary to examine the quality of the male seed. How is this latter to be produced? It is possible, after ordinary conjugal intercourse, to withdraw from the vagina a part of the seminal fluid emitted by the husband. This method does not seem, in itself, contrary to the moral law, since the intercourse has taken place according to the rules of nature.

But many doctors do not favour this method, because the spermatozoa run the risk of being damaged by the acidity of the vaginal secretions and of thus furnishing defective matter for examination.

They will therefore demand intercourse while wearing a sheath, and even then they will fear the action of the rubber on the spermatozoa; or they will demand interrupted intercourse or masturbation of the husband.

We content ourselves with simply saying here that these last three methods of obtaining the male seed are irreconcilable with the requirements of the moral law. We shall later give the reasons why this is so.

2. The cause of sterility, or at least serious indications of its origin, having been discovered, it remains to adopt the means which best favour the normal exercise of the laws of nature. Sometimes, to remedy this defect, recourse is had to the aid of a special surgical instrument, to introduce the male seed into the uterine cervix. But we return to the problem already indicated in the preceding paragraph. How is this seed obtained? It is always lawful, after ordinary intercourse, to take the fluid in the vagina and project it farther forward. There are a few dissenting voices in this matter among the theologians, but nearly all are unanimous in recognising the legitimacy of this operation.

But the doctors are dissatisfied. Many of them are unwilling to take the chance of provoking serious infections, because such an operation gives no guarantee of asepsis and it is well known how susceptible from this point of view are the uterus, the tubes and the ovaries. Thus, recourse is once more had to the already mentioned procedures for the examination of the seed; masturbation, the use of a sheath, interrupted intercourse.

We can now discuss these techniques at some length, from the standpoint of the moral law.

For a great number of doctors – they have no monopoly of the opinion, however – masturbation is an action completely devoid of any importance, provided it is not repeated indefinitely under the impulse of morbid obsessions and does not produce a state of pathological depression in the person who practises it. Very frequent in the case of the youth, this act reappears in the course of life every time that relations with the other sex are interrupted for a lengthy period; because, for the majority of men, sexual needs are practically incoercible and must be satisfied, if even in a very imperfect manner. Thus, it is only under the influence of moral and religious prejudices whose origin goes back to some unknown primitive taboo, that one sees it is precisely this unjustified reprobation, received from his education, which provokes in the adolescent a sentiment of shame and decadence, when he has only given way to his most natural impulses.

We do not deny that, for certain young people, the practice of masturbation, even fairly frequently, does not inevitably entail a train of irremediable consequences in the development of character and personality. But is the question so easily solved as the description we have just given would lead us to believe? Indeed, it must be admitted that more than one husband who was asked to furnish a sample of seminal fluid, for spermoculture or for artificial insemination, refused to have recourse to masturbation, preferring the method of interrupted intercourse.[1] Will it be said that this repulsion is due merely to the survival of adolescent scruples and to a fear of relapsing into the sentiment of inferiority which they overcame with so much difficulty? We admit that this explanation would be valid in some cases; it is far from being satisfactory for all.

On the contrary, this repugnance seems normal to those who, knowing the history of the development of the individual, know also how the sexual instinct behaves in the course of that development.

We pass, in effect, through the narcissistic stage in which our attention is fixed almost exclusively on ourselves, to the stage characterised by overt interest in things and in others; we lose a largely individual interest and gain sentiments of altruism and disinterestedness, for we must fit ourselves into the pattern of social life. And at the same time, our reason, our conscience, gaining strength, becomes more capable of directing our biological powers.

Now, the sexual instinct, whose roots are so deep and so far-reaching, is *par excellence* a social instinct; all its riches, to be

1. Dr. Séguy notes (Semaine des Hôpitaux de Paris, 28 mai 1946, p. 908) that many husbands are very happy when it is found possible to dispense from all examination of the sperm.

awakened in us and fully developed, must needs be directed towards *another*, because this instinct is to a large extent, though not exclusively, the creator of the couple, the common life, the family. Thus, according to sexologists who are the most responsible and the most attentive to reality, the sexual instinct, accidents apart, ought to show the following characteristics at the period of maturity –

The physiological and psychological activity which define this instinct are directed towards the opposite sex; pleasure, happines are not intelligible apart from this union with the partner. Moreover, it is not in promiscuity that one finds the perfection of erotic conduct: 'donjuanism,' says Hesnard, 'as we have been able to account for it through individual analyses by depth psychology, reveals defective virility.' (*Traité de Sexologie*, p. 299.)

Undoubtedly, married life imposes sacrifices, and still more does the rearing of a family; it is only, however, in a lasting life led in common that the individual will find the best conditions for his full development. For it is then that the activities of the two partners are fixed, and that each becomes, or ought to become, for the other the centre of thought and attraction, the object of devotion and love.

We gather from this exposition that the first law of the sexual instinct is that it directs the whole being towards another. We can understand, in consequence, why the sexual act 'is very different from a psychical genital reflex.' 'If the erotic act,' says the author we have already quoted, 'is materially animal, it is at the same time a highly psychical act by reason of the specific sensibility, at once complex and intense, which it releases in the person.' 'Weighed at its proper human value, it appears as much more of the moral order than of the material' (*Ibid.*, p. 306). And Hesnard concludes: 'The sexual act is essentially a social act' (*Ibid.*, p. 307). Such is nature's order, as described by an observer who is not especially inspired by religious beliefs.

But this order is easily disturbed; at the beginning of each new stage of development, deviation is possible, and it is the same danger which shows itself under different forms. Instead of developing into a more and more complete alloeroticism; instead of forgetting one's self to fix the interest on another, one runs the risk of not relinquishing autoerotism, of remaining at a stage of infantile confusion. Isolated masturbation, solitary habits, narcissistic reveries, homosexuality, donjuanism, psychic impotence, as well as masks of infantilism, momentary or definitive failures, characterise this faulty development. Are we to take mediocrity, malformations, as our yardstick to establish what ought to be? Because many do not attach more importance to the sex act than to the act of eating or drinking, are we therefore to define the ideal in accordance with such terms? Because a number of young men indulge in masturbation without thinking anything of it, will further concern be considered unnecessary and, in the cases we are discussing, will it be thought that the interests at stake are sufficient for an exeption to a law so rarely observed? Certainly not. For we have seen that a type of adult person exists whose sexual development has been completed and who therefore presents the signs we have indicated. This type is the man who is normal according to the order of nature, and each person should aim at realising that type in himself. No one will deny that there are checks, deficiencies, repressions for which the subjects are not responsible, or at least whose effects they no longer control and which they cannot immediately correct. But to accept willingly acts which denote a lack of self-mastery, to rest content with an unfinished development of personality, is to admit tacitly that whoever wishes may realise the ideal, whoever wishes may pursue it at will, and there is no more to say on the matter. This is to affirm in action that this ideal does not impose itself as an absolute, and to destroy at a blow all moral obligation.

The Church had no need to wait for modern psychologists to tell her that the sex instinct is a social instinct; in her view, the complete sex act is only permitted in the carnal union of husband and wife, it being understood, moreover, that this intercourse should be given all possible chance of being fruitful.

It is thus that the Holy Office in 1929[1], concluding a long investigation of the matter, the stages of which we do not propose to trace here, declared that it is not permitted 'to procure directly selfpollution in order to obtain a sperm by means of

1. Acta Apostolicae Sedes, 1929, p. 490.

which a contagious disease, blennoragia, may be discovered and as far as possible cured.'

Holding to the spirit of this instruction, we shall reject both interrupted coitus and the use of a sheath for the collection of male semen, every time that the sperm thus obtained must serve only for the purposes of examination and of analysis. It is a separated or unfinished act, a deliberately infertile act, and therefore inadmissible.

The problem of artificial insemination with the sperm of the husband is more complex than the preceding case. The obtaining of the products necessary for that operation, by masturbation or interrupted coitus is, of course, to be considered illicit. On the whole, authors are in agreement that the principles enunciated in our exposition have general validity, and they therefore apply here. Masturbation, even for purposes of procreation, remains a solitary act. In interrupted coitus with extra-vaginal emission of the sperm,[1] the sexual attention of the husband is at first clearly turned to the wife, but he diverts that attention before the completion of the act. Perturbation is introduced into the psycho-physiological dynamism, and this is serious because it prevents the perfection of union. Hence the reason why interrupted coitus will be regarded as forbidden and as a form of the solitary act. And this process of reasoning among the theologians is confirmed by a decision of the Holy Office which, in 1897, declared that artificial fecundation was illicit.

But here an objection may occur to the mind. It is one we have met on all sides, and we shall attempt to set it out faithfully here, and to answer it.

Is the coherent and logical doctrine, summarised in the preceding pages, definitive in all its parts? Was it not, indeed, built up at a time when the problem of artificial insemination had not been posed? It was in the eighteenth century that Spallanzani (who was a priest) discovered the mechanism of artificial insemination. It was only towards the middle of the nineteenth century that theologians found it necessary to ask themselves if it was lawful to inseminate a woman artificially with her husband's

1. Coitus interrupted in such a way that, voluntarily, the entire emission of the seminal fluid occurs outside the vagina.

fluid, gathered outside normal sex relations. But in judging these cases of conscience caused by scientific progress, they remained very faithful to the old modes of reasoning. Up to then, interrupted coitus and masturbation had been condemned as pursuits of solitary pleasure, as egoistic acts and, in the first of these practices, as a means of avoiding conception. Were they capable of meeting a new problem with a new spirit? In effect, instead of judging masturbation and interrupted coitus solely in themselves, ought they not to be joined in a synthetic view to the end for which they are, in the circumstances, accomplished: the end of procreation? And would not this fact render them morally justified and acceptable? One of the moralists[1] of the second half of the nineteenth century, not by any means the least of his day, found this compelling: he taught that perhaps masturbation was permitted to the husband to furnish the necessary fluid for artificial insemination, and that, in such case, it was not a separated and solitary act because the semen thus obtained was used towards fecundation. But the declaration of the Holy Office, which we have just mentioned, is later than this and it gives a direction which is entirely opposed to it. Will the day come when as a result of reflection on the data of the problem, masturbation and interrupted coitus, exercised in the above conditions, will not be considered as intrinsically bad actions? This must not be considered as possible. For if, in such proceedings, the primary end of marriage is stressed, another law of conjugal life is violated – that which lays down that the sexual activity of the married must be exercised in and by carnal union. It is clear in the case of masturbation; as for interrupted coitus, the variation occasioned to the regular usage of marriage seems the main essential. Moreover, we have a document of the first importance to guide us in reaching any future decisions on this matter. In a discourse to the Sixth International Congress of Catholic doctors, on September 29th, 1949, Pope Pius XII has discussed the question of artificial insemination and has laid down clearly the principles which must direct all debate in this matter. Apart from one or two points which still remain doubtful, the discussions which have taken

1. Ballerini-Palmieri: Opus theologicum morale, Vol. VI, No. 1304. See also Berardi: Praxis Confessariorum, 2e edit., No. 5. 292.

place among theologians, in the course of the nineteenth and twentieth centuries, are finished.

All intervention by a third party having been excluded, the following is the teaching of the Sovereign Pontiff concerning artificial insemination with the semen of the husband –

1. *As to intention:* 'The mere fact that the result envisaged (that is to say, procreation) is attained by this means, does not justify the use of the means itself; nor is the desire of the couple, in itself legitimate, to have a child, sufficient to establish the legitimacy of having recourse to artificial insemination which would fulfil that desire.'

2. *As to the process itself:* 'There is no need to point out that the active element can never be lawfully procured by acts contrary to nature.'

'Although one cannot exclude new methods *a priori* simply because they are new, nevertheless, as regards artificial insemination, not only is extreme caution called for, but the matter must be absolutely excluded. In speaking thus, we do not imply that the use of certain artificial means designed either to facilitate the natural act, or to cause the natural act normally accomplished to attain its end, is necessarily forbidden.'

The Pope underlines, therefore, that all procreation with the married couple must be the fruit of a physical union accomplished according to the laws of nature.

Consequently, the acts against nature aimed at procuring the masculine seminal fluid – masturbation, for example – are to be regarded as illicit and morally prohibited.

Equally reprehensible are the methods which, while they are not acts against nature, obtain the seminal fluid without physical union; for example, the piercing of the spermatic ducts, or the use of the fluid from nocturnal pollutions.

The means whose effect is to help normally accomplished sexual concourse to attain its end, are not necessarily forbidden. It thus remains legitimate, as we have noticed above, to take the male fluid in the vagina and project it farther forward in the female genital ducts, for this is simply to complete a natural act.

How must we henceforward consider, from the moral point of view, the de Courty process, which consists in collecting the male reproductive elements in a preservative, during otherwise normal sexual relations, and then introducing it into the uterine cervix by means of an instrument?

In the second volume of *Mélanges de Science Religieuse* (Lille, 1944, p. 339 *et seq.*), Canon Tiberghien, Professor of Medical Deontology in the *Facultés libres de Lille*, has put forward the following justification of this method: 'The sexual organs,' he writes, 'have two functions: a function of procreation and a function of intimacy. It is not permitted to exercise one of these two functions while separating it from the other "by human artifice," according to the expression of *Casti Connubi*. Providence wishes that the human race should be reproduced in the embrace of love.'

'But,' he adds a little later, 'in order to pass judgment morally on the diverse cases which present themselves in this difficult matter, it must be remarked that abnormality and illegitimacy must not be confused, either as regards procreation or as regards intimacy. Everything which is abnormal (in the sense of unusual) is not illegitimate.' And he formulates this principle: 'An act which shows some anomalies, remains legitimate when its essential, intrinsic ends are respected and when these anomalies are justified by abnormal circumstances. Now' – (and this is the point he wishes to make) – 'in the de Courty process' – (that is to say, the one in which the sperm is collected in a condom during conjugal intercourse) – 'two anomalies are to be noted. The first consists in dividing the act of fecundation into two periods; but we have seen that this kind of anomaly is not considered by the theologians as rendering the intervention *per se* unlawful. The second anomaly is to a certain extent injurious to intimacy... This second anomaly cannot, however, be bracketed with the absolute separation which takes place, for example, in solitary indulgence. Here the organs really function *in* conjugal union. The double function of procreation and of intimacy are therefore essentially respected, and the anomalies seem sufficiently justified by the abnormal circumstances.' (Pp. 341–342).

And after having answered some possible objections, our author concludes: 'If the question is squarely faced up to, it will be seen that the objections raised against the de Courty method are all motivated by a preliminary conviction that the process employed could be used to serve anti-conceptional purposes. Doubtless this is so, but the abuse does not condemn the correct usage. Now, it is a fact that here the impeached process tends only *to aid nature* in its effort at fecundation.' (P. 344).

The Pope's discourse is concerned only with the formulation of general principles; it does not directly decide the unlawfulness of this process and of some others.[1] Nevertheless, it must be admitted that the arguments in favour of this method seem now very insecure. Indeed, the authority of the Sovereign Pontiff comes to buttress the doctrine which, basing itself on the requirements of the natural law, held that one must not disturb in any way the functioning of the genital organs as fixed by nature, in the course of conjugal relations. If artificial insemination is necessary and possible, it must take place either beforehand, by the treatment of weaknesses and malformations, or afterwards, as has already been said, by supplying the deficiencies of the physiological mechanism.

The whole problem, therefore, is to decide whether, in the de Courty process, there is an act of sexual congress which can be called natural. We admit that the process appears to safeguard intimacy sufficiently; but it seems to us that procreation is here sought in a manner which is too indirect. We are no longer concerned with a help given to nature's work, but with a real correction. And the teaching of the Pope does not allow this to be accepted.

3. When a definite azoospermia has been established in the case of a husband, has one reached the end of one's resources? From the simple viewpoint of technique, evidently not, for a solution immediately comes to mind – that of attempting the fecundation of the woman with semen provided by some one other than the husband, by a third party or 'donor.' And to-day when the principles of the moral law are so often considered as

1. In an article of the *Nouvelle Revue Théologique* 1949, p. 1,072 *et seq.*, 'Insémination Artificielle et Documents Pontificaux,' Rev. Père Renwart, S.J., has given the most complete historical exposition available of the diverse opinions held on this question by the theologians of the nineteenth and twentieth century, as well as a remarkably precise commentary on the Discourse of Pius XII.

devoid of value by so many of our contemporaries, it is not surprising that the idea has been carried out in practice. The method is frequently employed in Anglo-Saxon countries: it was also employed in Hitlerite Germany, and it shows a tendency to spread in France. Nevertheless, the judgment that must be passed on this method in the name of the moral law is not for a single moment in doubt. Hetero-insemination constitutes an essential violation of the laws of marriage.

Let it be noticed, first of all, that the only method by which the seminal fluid can be procured in the present case, is the masturbation of the donor. We have already shown why masturbation must be declared inacceptable, even when there is question of the artificial insemination of a wife by her husband. All the more reason, then, when there is question of a stranger. This solitary functioning of the genital organs is not lawful in any case, and one has never the right voluntarily to perform this act.

But even if technical skill allowed for the gathering in sufficient quantity of reproductive elements, without having recourse to masturbation, the attempt to inseminate a woman with semen other than that of her husband would remain unlawful. For, in spite of certain appearances, we are there faced with veritable adultery.

We admit that, in many cases, this character of conjugal infidelity is not recognised by the partners in marriage, when the question arises in circumstances such as we have described. Even though the idea of this measure did not originate with him, and even if he accepts the arrangement without enthusiasm, the husband will but rarely raise objections in principle against this procedure. He will see it as a means of adopting a child and as a remedy for the nervous condition of his wife who will find, in this way, the satisfaction of her need for maternity. They are indeed very few who would suspect that in doing this they are failing in the promises which they gave to each other. In particular, the husband will not feel an awakening of jealousy because of the project although jealousy comes only too readily to a great number of men. It is merely that the modalities of commonplace adultery are absent.[1] The symbolical physical giving and the

1. Nevertheless, many doctors remark that married people, even when they are resigned to artificial fecundation by a 'donor', are not without a certain malaise.

expression of that fuller giving is reserved to the husband and wife. Why, then, should they be alarmed? It is not a third coming between them. And couples have been met with who were so satisfied with a first experience and with a first child resulting from this experience, that they had recourse to the method again.

Are we to attribute the ease of this acceptance to a diminution of moral sense, to a dimming of conscience which leads the men of our time to judge the value of actions by their immediate results? Or is it quite simply due to a surprise of the faculties of appreciation disconcerted by the strange novelty of these techniques? The two explanations are probably complementary. There is no lack of voices, moreover, to proclaim loudly the legitimacy of this procedure. Already on February 15th, 1930, E. Douay wrote in *La Gazette Médicale de France:* 'In the case of definitive azoospermia, there can be two eventualities. The wife knows the cause of the conjugal sterility; and if she demands her right to maternity, she must either divorce her husband or be unfaithful to him or obtain pregnancy through artificial insemination. If the husband is consulted, it is the last alternative which he will accept to save his marriage. Artificial fecundation, far from being immoral, will allow the household union to be preserved and at the same time save appearances...'

Let us see what the moral law demands. One is free to enter matrimony or not to do so. But if one chooses to do so, one must respect the rules which it involves. The engagement of marriage has the full form of a contract; but the parties are not empowered to change the essential dispositions either at the moment when the contract is made, or later on, because this contract causes the parties to enter on a state of life whose purposes and laws are fixed by nature and by the Author of nature.

Left to themselves, the instinctive and sentimental forces which bring the man and the woman together would not suffice to create marriage. Love desires union and perpetuity of union. But for a long time now, the ambiguity of this tendency and the fact that there are two loves have been concealed. One love is the giving of self, the desire to devote and even to sacrifice oneself for another; the other love is an exploitation, a monopoly, sometimes destructive of the person loved. That is why love will attain the end of its most profound aspirations, the symbiosis of two beings, on every plane, only if it submits to discipline, and if the instinctive impulse and the sentimental *élan* are not left to their own devices but directed by the mind. And – let us face reality – the 'sublimation' of these equivocal forces, for the majority of men, will be accomplished only by accepting the charges of a stable and fecund conjugal life. Fidelity will be opposed to sexual vagabondage; the egoism of two people will be broken by the coming of children. But all is not then finished. The end of the process is not the birth and nurture of the child, but his education; here the instinctive stage must give place to conscious maternity and paternity. The man, the adult, the 'vir,' is he who has taken on a life responsibility for a woman and for the children born of his union with that woman. This is the bond which the partners accept at the time of marriage, if they sincerely desire to enter upon it in the spirit of Christian teaching. And here again the Church safeguards the requirements of nature. There is a tendency to regard the conjugal act as the crown of the love exchange, the most perfect manifestation of the giving of self, while considering the act solely in itself and apart from all its possible consequences. We would have many reservations to make with regard to that theory; but to confine ourselves to the matter in hand, is it not frequently experienced that, apart from exceptional cases, the married couple are more profoundly joined one to the other if they have had a child together than if their relations remained sterile? Could it be otherwise, and is it not the child who gives full meaning to conjugal love?

May we be permitted to quote a fine passage from Dr. Biot where this law is remarkably described and analysed: 'This complete realisation of the human couple allows the transmission of life; as father and mother, they are respectively a better man and a better woman than they were as a young husband and a young wife without children. If further proof is needed, it comes with the words which this woman murmurs to him whom she loves with a full and true love: 'I wish to have a child by you.' Not just: 'I wish to have a child,' as would be the case if only biological sexuality were speaking in her, if it were only the call of the species making itself heard in her love. But rather: 'I wish to have a child by you.' This is surely a clear indication that her wish amalgamated the two elements – her desire for maternity and her love; that the child will have its full value only if the giving of self, of which it is the fruit, arises from far beyond the flesh, from far beyond the instinct for the multiplication of life, because it originates with the person beloved. She loves, in the person of her husband, at once the lover whose caresses she seeks, the man who will render her physiologically fecund, the spouse from whom she receives the incomparable moral aureola of maternity, and the partner whom, by the procreation of a child, she spiritually exalts.

'For his part, equally, if he wishes to analyse fully the sentiment which animates him and reason back to all the ends included in his instinct, the husband will love in his wife the woman who makes him know the joys of union, the developed and ripe being she has become through the implanting in her of a new life, and the spouse who, by making him a father, ennobles him and makes him lift himself to better things.' (*Le Corps et l'Âme*, pp. 171–172.) 'This perpetuity which love demands,' writes Maurice Blondel, 'this indissoluble and living union – behold it, then, in the child.' (*L'Action*, p. 258.) And we conclude with the same philosopher, that the end of love is not love, but the family; that is to say, the community of parents in the service of the child.

Union by means of the children which they have from one another and which they bring up together, such, according to the teaching of the Church, is the order of nature for the welding together of the sexes.

Of course, marriage is not forbidden to anyone, even to certain sterile persons, on condition that normal conjugal relations can be established; but, it must be admitted, a sterile marriage is an imperfect marriage. And the norm of a state of life is not reckoned according to exceptions and half-successes, but according to the generality of cases: *ut in pluribus*, as St. Thomas says.

At the moment when they exchange their matrimonial consent,

the parties undertake an agreement – the one that he will be the father of children born to the woman, the other that she will be the mother of children begotten by this man. Now, it is in fecundation that the union is accomplished which makes the man and the woman henceforward father and mother of the same child. The parties, therefore, promise to one another exclusive fecundation – that the ovum of the wife will be fertilised only by the sperm of the husband and that he, in his turn, will fertilise only the ovum of the wife.

By the marriage consent, a woman therefore excludes all sexual relations with any man except her husband, and to fail in this promise is adultery; but she engages herself just as firmly not to have children except by him, and failure here is also adultery.

Thus it is clearly seen what the answer must be, if the objection is raised that the husband consents. These are inalienable rights, and the husband and wife, even though they may be in full agreement on the matter, have no power to modify in any way whatever the essential dispositions of marriage. The woman would not be free from guilt because her husband had consented to her having relations with another man; and the case is the same for artificial insemination with the semen of a 'donor.'

For completeness, we must return to this latter. By an action to which he attaches perhaps the least importance, he has given the products which will serve for the artificial insemination of an unknown woman. This action of his is contrary to the Moral Law, and more seriously so than a simple act of masturbation. This is so because, if the woman is made pregnant, he – the father according to the flesh – has made up his mind to take no interest whatsoever in his child. He refuses to observe the law which requires that man, in exercising his physical activities, should do so under the discipline of the spirit, that he may thus raise himself to a completely human order of conduct. This donor fully and freely consents to lower himself to the rôle of producer, of stallion. And we have there an example of what modern technical skill, emancipated from morality, can make of man.

It is clear that insemination of the unmarried woman is also inadmissible. 'The natural law and the Divine positive law,' recalls Pius XII in the discourse cited above, 'are such that

procreation of a new life must be the fruit of marriage alone.'
The child needs a father, not for his physical life alone, but above
all to watch over his physical and emotional development. To
create orphans deliberately is certainly to run counter to one of
the most profound demands of human nature. Accidents independent of our will create a sufficiency of sad situations in this
matter. It would be a culpable cruelty to increase voluntarily the
number of these unbalanced human situations.

All that we have said about the donor in connection with a
married woman, therefore, holds good here. In both cases, his
act cannot be justified as it is incompatible with the most ele-
mentary moral sense.

These appraisals which we have just made of the various forms
of artificial insemination, and which we believe to be commanded
by the moral law, will probably appear very misleading to more
than one of our readers, doctors or biologists.

Why, in the name of abstract principles and very complicated
reasoning, should we discourage and drive even to despair those
whose only desire is to propagate life, and that at a time when
neo-Malthusian ideas have such influence in our country?

The theologian is not, as many would have us think, insensible
to these appeals and to this distress. Usually, he does not shut
himself away with his books; he knows how to leave them. In
addition to his studies, he often fulfils the rôle of counsellor and
of doctor to souls. He knows the individual case as well as any-
body does – he has watched the person, bewildered by passion or
suffering, broken by the blows of life, silently striving or hardening
in silence before his very eyes. And when he meets a question like
that just raised, with a negative answer based on the principle:
'the end does not justify the employing of means which morality
condemns,' it is himself, as well as his questioner, whom he
answers, reminding himself that he cannot allow himself to be
betrayed by his pity into a dereliction of duty. He is not the
master of the law, and he must obey it as others must.

Such an attitude can only be understood when seen in the
setting of an ensemble which forms part of a general conception
of the world. The requirements of morality make sense only if it
is remembered that there is an infinitely powerful and good God

who harmonises all the disorder and suffering of humanity so that, in the long run, all works out for the good of man.

REV. PÈRE TESSON S.J.
*Professeur de Théologie morale
à l'Institut Catholique de Paris*

DISCOURSE OF HIS HOLINESS POPE PIUS XII.
FOURTH INTERNATIONAL CONGRESS OF
CATHOLIC DOCTORS

Rome, September 29th, 1949

There is a profound significance which is a great source of joy to Us, dear sons, in your being assembled here with Us. The fact that thirty different nations are represented here, while yet the rifts created by the pre-war and post-war years are far from being filled; the fact that you are come to speak to Us of the lofty ideas which direct your exchange of views in the medical world; finally, the fact that you are exercising in that world something more than a simple profession, in fact a true and excellent ministry of charity – all this is certainly of a nature to assure on Our part a most paternal welcome. Together with Our benediction, you are expecting that We shall give you some advice about your duties. We shall content Ourselves with putting before you some brief reflections on the obligations imposed on you by the progress of medicine, the beauty and grandeur of its exercise, and its relations with natural and Christian morality.

The progress of medicine

For many centuries, and above all in our epoch, medicine has made ceaseless progress. That progress is certainly a complex one, whose object includes the most varied branches of theory and of practice: progress in the study of the body and its constitution; in all the physical, chemical, and natural sciences; in the knowledge of cures, their properties and the methods of applying them; progress in the application of the reciprocal actions and reactions of the physical and the moral, not only to the therapeutics of physiology, but to that of psychology as well.

Anxious to neglect no iota of the advantages furnished by this progress, the doctor is continually on the watch for all the means of healing, or at least of assuaging, the diseases and the suffering of mankind. As a surgeon, he strives to render less painful the operations which he performs; as a gynaecologist, he endeavours to lessen the sufferings of the confinement, without ever imperilling the health of the mother or the child, and without running the risk of altering the feelings of maternal tenderness for the new-born baby. The spirit of pure humanity, the natural love for his fellow-men, enlivens and guides every conscientious doctor in his researches; what, then, will be the attitude of the Christian doctor, inspired by divine charity to devote himself, sparing neither self nor effort, to the good of those whom he regards as his brothers both naturally and according to the faith? He rejoices wholeheartedly, of course, in the immense progress already made, in the results previously obtained by his predecessors and sought to-day by his colleagues, with whom he is at one in the continuation of a magnificent tradition, and legitimately proud also of the contribution he himself has made. However, he never sits down in satisfaction, because he always sees before him new steps to be taken and fresh advances to be made. Towards this end, he works with passionate earnestness, as a doctor consecrated to the relieving of humanity and of each individual man; as a *savant* who ecstatically tastes 'the joy of knowing,' when discovery comes on the heels of discovery; as a believer, a Christian, who, in the splendours which he discovers, in the new horizons which extend before him till they are lost to sight, knows how to read the grandeur and power of the Creator, the inexhaustible goodness of the Father Who, having given to the living organism all the resources it needs to develop, to defend itself, to cure itself spontaneously in the majority of cases, causes it also to discover in lifeless or living nature – mineral, vegetable, animal – remedies for bodily ailments.

The beauty and grandeur of the practice of medicine
The doctor would not respond fully to the ideal of his vocation if, while making profitable use of the most recent discoveries in medical science and art, he brought into play, in his rôle of practitioner, only his intelligence and his skill, and failed to bring in also – we would even say above all – his human heart and that charitable delicacy which belongs to him as a Christian. He does not work *in anima vili*; he acts directly on bodies, it is true, but

on bodies which are each animated by an immortal, spiritual soul, and – in virtue of the mysterious but indissoluble connection between the physical and the moral – his action is efficacious on the body only if he acts at the same time on the soul.

Whether he is dealing with the body or with the human composite in its unity, the Christian doctor will be always on his guard against the fascination of technique, against the temptation to apply his knowledge and his art to other ends than the treatment of the patients entrusted to him. Thank God, he will never have to be on his guard against another, a criminal, temptation to use, in the service of base interests, unavowable passions and inhuman crimes, the gifts hidden by God in the heart of nature. We have not, alas, to seek very far in order to find concrete cases of these hateful abuses. The splitting of the atom and the production of atomic energy, for example, is one thing; its destructive use, free from all control, is quite another matter. The magnificent progress of the most modern technique of aviation is one thing; quite another matter is the large-scale use of bomber squadrons, without its being possible to confine their action to military and strategic objectives. Above all, respectful investigation, which reveals the beauty of God in the mirror of His works, His power in the forces of nature, is one thing; but the deification of this nature and of maternal forces in the negation of their Author, is a different matter entirely.

How, on the other hand, does the doctor act who is worthy of his vocation? He seizes on these same forces and natural properties in order to achieve, by means of them, cure, health, and vigour; and often, which is more precious still, to take preventive steps against diseases, contagions, or epidemics. At his command is the formidable power of radioactivity, to be used for the cure of diseases resistant to all other treatment; he has at hand the properties of the most virulent poisons to serve in the preparation of efficacious remedies; nay more, the germs of the most dangerous infections are used in every kind of way, in serotherapy and in vaccination.

The relations of medicine with natural and Christian morality

Finally, natural and Christian morality have everywhere their imprescriptible rights. It is from them, and not from any considerations of feelings or of materialist, naturalist philanthropy, that the essential principles of medical deontology are derived: the dignity of the human body, the fraternity of all men, the sovereign dominion of God over life and destiny.

We have already had many occasions to touch on a great number of particular points concerning medical morality. Here is a question which has become of the first interest, and which demands, no less urgently than the others, the light of Catholic moral doctrine: the question of artificial insemination. We cannot allow the present opportunity to pass without indicating, briefly and in broad outline, the judgment of morality on this matter.

1. The practice of this artificial insemination, when it concerns a human being, cannot be considered, either exclusively or even principally, from the biological and medical point of view, while ignoring that of morality and of right.

2. Artificial insemination, outside marriage, is to be condemned purely and simply as immoral.

The Natural Law and the Divine Positive Law lay down that the procreation of a new life may be the fruit of marriage only. Marriage alone safeguards the dignity of husband and wife (particularly of the wife, in the present case), and their personal welfare. Of itself, it alone provides for the welfare and upbringing of the child.

Consequently, there is no divergence of opinion possible among Catholics about the condemnation of artificial insemination outside marriage. The child conceived in these conditions by that very fact would be illegitimate.

3. Artificial insemination in marriage, but produced by the active element of a third person, is equally immoral, and, as such, to be condemned outright.

The husband and wife have *alone* a reciprocal right over their bodies in order to engender a new life; and this right is exclusive, untransferable, inalienable. This ought to be so too from consideration for the child. Nature imposes on the person, who gives life to a baby, the duty of its conservation and of its education, by very reason of the bond established. But no bond of origin, no moral and juridical bond of conjugal procreation, exists between the legitimate husband and the child who is the fruit of the active element of a third party – even in the case where the husband has given his consent.

4. As to the lawfulness of artificial insemination in marriage, let it suffice for the moment that We recall to your minds these principles of the Natural Law: the mere fact that the result envisaged is attained by this means, does not justify the use of the means itself; nor is the desire of the husband and wife to have a child – in itself a very legitimate desire – sufficient to prove the legitimacy of having recourse to artificial insemination, which would fulfil this desire.

It would be wrong to hold that the possibility of having recourse to this means would render valid the marriage between persons incapable of contracting it because of *impedimentum impotentiae*.

On the other hand, there is no need to point out that the active element can never be lawfully procured by acts contrary to nature.

Although one cannot exclude new methods *a priori* simply because they are new, nevertheless, as regards artificial insemination, not only is extreme caution called for, but the matter must be absolutely dismissed. In speaking thus, We do not imply that the use of certain artificial means solely destined either to facilitate the natural act or to cause the natural act normally accomplished to attain its end, are necessarily forbidden.

Let it not be forgotten that the procreation of a new life according to the will and plan of the Creator, *alone* brings with it, and that to an astonishing degree of perfection, the realisation of the ends pursued. It is at once in conformity with the corporal and spiritual nature and the dignity of husband and wife, and with the normal and happy development of the child.

Your sincerely religious spirit, and your coming here to-day, are a pledge of your unwavering fidelity to all the duties of Catholic doctors, and also a pledge of your willingness to contribute, by your example and your influence, to promote, among your colleagues and your disciples, among your patients and their families, the principles which inspire yourselves. It is with this confidence that, with the paternal effusion of Our heart, We give to you, to all those whom you represent here, to your families, to all those who are dear to you, Our Apostolic Benediction.

Note: in English Civil Law the child conceived as a result of artificial insemination by a party other than the husband would be held to be illegitimate. – EDITOR.

Death

EDITOR'S FOREWORD

Once when I was ill a young medical colleague brought me a book to while away the idle hours, Goethe's *Death*. Since then it has been a subject which I have not willingly considered in its material aspects or, perhaps I should say, in its dematerialising aspects. Except during the brief period of his internship, the average doctor and more particularly the specialist or consultant never sees a death. It is true that they attend to the preliminaries and forecast the event but rarely are they actually present at the moment of dissolution. None the less there arise two main problems which the doctor has to solve in the forum of his conscience: The patient warned that he must soon die is frequently the one who has no belief or almost no belief in the realities of the after life. As often as not he confesses this, somewhat shyly it may be, to his medical attendant. In doing so it seems to me that he thereby confesses to a hope that the latter, whose education and worldly experience he respects, may be able and willing to assist him to a solution of the problem. Too often no attempt is made to help him. The penalty of success in medical practice is usually that one has no time for the purely human values; the best 'bedside manner' as often as not conceals a wholly necessary impersonal relation to one's patients. I do not suggest that doctors are unfeeling or callous but they do have to develop a certain power of 'turning the other way,' lest a too personal relation to the patient impair their judgment; which is why surgeons will not operate on near relatives. To continue, let me say that when the patient faced with approaching decease expresses himself in doubt as to his life after death or when this doubt can be surmised in the patient, the doctor has now an opportunity of assuring him that there is much to hope for in the future life and that there are people who are only too willing and able to assist him to find out the answer to the problem which for him has now assumed a certain urgency. This is the time to speak with confidence and assurance of one's beliefs, to assert conclusions leaving the examination of the premises leading to them to others with more time for and experience in their exposition.

Once started on an enquiry that is all important for him, the patient will follow up the matter for himself with a very little encouragement. Yes; we possess all the answers. Let us not be too diffident about sharing them with others in their need.

All this presupposes that the patient is aware of the precarious condition of his physical health and, unfortunately, there are many who will conspire to conceal it from him; some blatantly believing that they do well; others stifling their consciences with the argument that he will realise his condition himself as he gets weaker. We must die; it is all important that we die well. It must be clearly asserted that for anyone to conceal the truth in such cases from the person most concerned is sinful. I have always told my patients the truth and I have never had a case where the telling of it harmed the patient. Many of them thanked me for my frankness and I have abundant evidence that great moral and spiritual good accrued to those who thus were enabled to prepare for the most important event of their conscious terrestrial lives.

The Church provides great spiritual aids for the dying and hopes that they will do so actively embracing their Faith and turning their last thoughts to their Lord and Saviour Jesus Christ in whom lies all our hope. Having called on all the Saints to assist the dying person she continues: 'Go forth Christian soul from this world in the name of God the Father Almighty who created thee; in the name of Jesus Christ who suffered for thee; in the name of the Holy Ghost who was infused into thee,' etc.... then as the soul departs, she prays that the angels and saints will bear this soul into the sight of God – 'may Christ who called thee receive thee.' Those who have witnessed a truly Christian death will remember it as something noble, fine; a source of edification and consolation rather than of gloom and despondency. Death is but the beginning of life. The Church teaches that we shall rise again in glory with Christ in our own bodies at the Last Day; that for us, therefore, death is really the beginning of a new and greater life. There are many who arrive at death's door still weighted by the burden of their sins; let us not be among those who would conceal from their minds the information which by His Grace might help to turn their wills to God.   EDITOR

PREFACE TO FRENCH EDITION

The indifference and the almost defensive attitude of our contemporaries towards death, that unique moment in the life of every man, are the expression of a materialist conception of human life. The Christian is conscious of the miseries and the weaknesses of man, of the forces which penetrate and govern him – world forces, life forces, forces of society; but the Christian will not accept this reduction to the biological and the social.

It is to answer the scandal of a world in which death no longer appears in a Christian perspective, that the *Cahiers Laënnec* published, in their issue of December, 1946, different articles expressing the views of the doctor, the philosopher, and the priest. This *Cahier* having been exhausted, we reissue now the principal articles which then appeared.

DEATH IN THE HOSPITAL

The memory of the first contact with death remains for a long time in the memory of the young doctor. Grown to his full stature, having ascended several degrees in the hierarchy of the hospital, with his experience enriched by all those deaths of which he has been the witness or even the cause, he remembers nevertheless, this grey-haired patient whom he used to see every day in the row of beds on the left of the main ward, and who he was told was a heart case. He recalls a certain day when, in the course of an observation lecture with the chief of the clinic, the man called out for help. The nurse having arrived, the group of young doctors moved away, led by the chief. These latter, bewildered every morning by maladies the names of which they were hearing for the first time, by the verdicts and by the clinical examinations still so new to them, followed the chief, so sure of himself and apparently so competent. A few words – 'angina pectoris'; a nod of that self-approbation of one who knows; an anguished face scarcely noticed, and the last struggling for breath were there. The grey-haired patient had become a corpse. With an ever steady hand the senior unhooked the chart, signed the death certificate, and led his band two beds farther on to some new observation. A moment later there was a loud and clear voiced discussion of the signs of portal obstruction.

I remember, however, that nurse still affected by the death, since her whole attitude, even though she accompanied us, showed that she was still thinking of it. I remember also those fellow-students who exchanged impressions on what, for us, was an event but which did not seem to have disturbed the life of the ward, for no one was concerned. Those in the neighbouring beds continued to read, absorbed in *La Vie Parisienne* or *Frou-Frou*; a boy was distributing slices of bread; a ward-maid was conducting a visitor who gave the very decided impression that he was not going to allow himself to be upset. In a corner, down there, a 'sortant' who perhaps had known the other 'sortant' (one who goes out feet first, as the saying is) looked fixedly before him. The familiar sounds had not changed. The only slightly unusual activity was that someone was bringing forward some screens to conceal the washing of the corpse. But life went on as usual. At most, the *Lamereaux* ward had numbered, for a few moments, one patient less.

Since then, the pictures of other deaths have been confused in my mind. There have been, however, more atrocious deaths – a little boy crushed by a lorry, a bag of skin without skeleton, lying for the consultation on a stretcher, his mother beside him; there have been slower deaths – interminable agonies, pains, cold sweats making the skin viscous; more spectacular deaths – the whole ward following the development of unexpected drama; silent deaths – when the patient simply did not resume his place in the bed he had quitted for the operating theatre...

But I have always kept the memory of that first death, and of the hardness of heart, the dryness of men.

The patient being dead, the nurse must reckon the time the toilet will take; the house-surgeon must reckon the chances of a postmortem examination; the superintendent must take steps to avoid a theft. The work is not finished because the patient has died. New cares arise, as is normal.

What shocked me, what still nearly always shocks me, is the apparent indifference – very apparent, placarded even – which each adopts. Death is an embarrassment. Should one allow oneself to be impressed by it? Ought not this horror to be hidden from those gravely ill, and therefore from all? Ought it not to be resisted, both individually and socially? Is it not a good thing that the hum of conversation, the noise of accessories – the hairdresser, the trollies, the telephones – should rise higher than before? Is it not natural that each should evade this lesson and turn as quickly as possible to the shallows of humdrum life? We quickly recover lightheartedness – as always – and it is nearly always thus.

Sometimes a nurse who loves her profession, a house-surgeon who is attached to his patients, a patient in a neighbouring bed who has a kind heart, manifests for a few minutes a certain emotion or a certain respect. But the mass fear to show this sympathy, this charity, this respect which shares in the event. Individual reactions are often touching; the herd, save for a few exceptions, remains as unmoved as a wall. It does not wish to weaken, and it keeps a stiff upper-lip of indifference at the price of a certain amount of muzzling.

I am well aware that, when possible, the most solitary corners are reserved for those who are dying. This is a matter of propriety; one is screened from the meagre warmth coming from the crowd…

There is no possible regulation to improve this. The regulation is there merely to assure that the man is really dead. It demands that a house-surgeon should come to state this; and if, at three o'clock on a winter's morning, a very obvious corpse is brought into the hospital, the rule is there to demand that the house-surgeon, who perhaps has just retired to rest after three hours in the operating theatre, should make a declaration of something obvious to all. To revenge himself for this useless disturbance, the house-surgeon is advised, in his turn, to call for the presence of a police representative, or to impose on the staff the pretence of energetic resuscitation treatment and a hot mustard bath of an already frozen corpse, for a good hour. Such is the regulation and the reactions which it provokes. There is no concern with death, but only with its legal aspects, however absurd.

Many patients refuse to die in hospital. Their families take them home a little before death. This practice is detestable in that it removes all hope of post-mortem verification, and thus denies to the doctor an opportunity of something which is absolutely fundamental to progress.

But such conduct is understandable. It is touching. It carries the proof that, in face of death, another attitude can be hoped for in place of this hardness, this indifference or this collective muzzling.

In his own home, the patient will be the centre of a family circle – or of a nest of vipers. Whether or not he expresses some last commandments to his family, some last wishes for his own, or a final malediction; whether or not he adds a new saw to the catalogue of the wisdom of the ancients; whether his death is that of the just or the miserable – in any case, he will be the focus of love, of interest, of desires and of affliction. He will not die solitary in the midst of a crowd. Those about him will pay attention to him. For a fleeting moment, life will pause around him.

It is said that in hospital the patient dies like a dog; that is rarely quite exact, and if it were true, the patient would not always be aware of it. He is probably fully occupied with himself and those whose task it is are materially as concerned for him.

Death in the hospital dishonours, not the dying, but the living who refuse to share in the tragic moment. Everything which blots the grandeur of that moment taints the assistants. The degradation of this dramatic moment bears witness to the debasement of a certain public conscience. Fear is the cause of this. Something sacred has been defiled.

Jacob awakes from his sleep and says –

> 'Of a truth, the Lord was in this place,
> And as for me, I knew it not.'

Then seized with fear, he adds –

> 'How dreadful is this place!
> It is indeed the House of God,
> It is indeed the Gate of Heaven.'
> (Gen. 28. 16–18).

(Extract from the personal notes of a young doctor)

THE DOCTOR IN RELATION
TO DEATH

'We are all here for death: such is life – *c'est la vie*, eh, Captain?'
The humble rigger who spoke those moving and profound words
to his officer stricken with a cruel loss was right in thus leavening
the sorrowful tragedy with hope. He recalls also to us our
common condition which brings nearer to each other in a singu-
lar way, before this awful mystery, the doctor and the patient.

Our profession, however, finds the reason of its being in the
service of life; it fights against death, against everything which
threatens health, in accidents or in sickness. For the doctor, this
daily fight becomes as a second nature, and some would think
that, when the doctor and death confront each other, there can
only result on his part a fierce and stubborn opposition to this
ancient enemy whom we are accustomed to fight on every front
and in all circumstances. If, in spite of all our knowledge and
all our devotion, it defeats us, ought we not then revolt? This
attitude would be logical, if it rested with the doctor, the
officer in the service of life, really to conquer death. But his finest
successes are never more than a truce which death accords to him,
and sooner or later it will have the last word. I have known
splendid doctors, heroically devoted to their patients, who were
revolted by death as by a personal injury, a treason, an injustice.

If it is true that death must remain, in the eyes of us doctors,
the great enemy against which we must fight with all our resources, backed by patiently acquired knowledge, our minds
made alert by our experience of the whole field of life, is it reasonable that we should be indignant, that we should indulge in
barren irritation, before this inescapable condition of human
existence? Must we despair 'like those who are without hope,'
because we do not open our eyes to a clearer and higher
truth?

It is indeed absolutely conceivable that an atheist doctor
should take up this attitude; but a Christian doctor ought to go
beyond mere appearances, and acting towards his condemned

patients according to other lights, he can say with St. Paul: 'O death, where is thy victory?'

It is curious, however, that one finds among unbelievers the most contradictory attitudes. They are in revolt because of their patients' death; and yet these same doctors, in the name of pure sophism, are the purveyors of death, since they are concerned in criminal abortions, or even 'therapeutic' abortions, or again euthanasia.

I prefer the paradox of the Christian doctor who, while submitting to our human lot, remains in spite of that always and everywhere, in every circumstance, a respecter of life, its defender and protector. He knows, indeed, that death does not annihilate the whole being, that it merely removes it from the activities of natural life, deprives it of possibilities, checks the account of good and evil but allows the judgment and the debt to remain. He knows that while life continues, everything in and about us can be modified; and that the appearance of a new life, as it were the rebound of an instant in a life that is finishing, can propagate itself to the ends of the earth. Since death which we cannot suppress recalls to us the presence of the Master of Life and of this Death, we shall behave towards it as towards Him, in order that we may become for those whom He confides to us the modest instruments of His mercy and of His love. It will be easy for us to rise from the body to the soul, from the flesh to the spirit, from the visible to the invisible. The life which we serve as doctors will certainly appear to us as something precious, but not as the supreme good, not as Life in its plenitude. We shall understand the virtue of sacrifice and that 'he who will save his life will lose it, and he that will lose his life will save it.'

Let us, Christian doctors, take up therefore an attitude to death which is logical, loyal, courageous, in the steps of Him who is the *Way*, the *Truth* and the *Life*. Let us remember that death is not an end but a beginning, and that preparation, initiation are needed for this re-birth. This can be the work of a whole life; happy those for whom it is so. But it can also be the fruit of an illumination, an acceptance, in the last moment of life. The Christian doctor who can assure this moment has the imperious duty of dispelling from it, if he can, all darkness.

The Way

Christ said: 'I am the Way.' There is, then, only one Way. All the others end either in a blind alley of meaningless, or in an abyss. When the Christian doctor is faced with death, the way is fully traced for him; respect for a life that does not belong to us; enlightened and steadfast combat to maintain life as long as there is a breath to reveal it; human and Christian alleviation of the rupture, which he knows is but temporary, between the soul and the body; – a serving, then of both the body and the soul.

The way of unbelief or even of indifference is full of contradictions. In revolt against death, the doctor in this way has only one preoccupation, to veil the face of death from his patient by deceiving him, and if necessary even by reducing his sensibility to the point of obscuring the perceptive powers of his mind. He runs the risk of masking and perhaps even hastening the fatal instant, through an action which he believes to be charitable, by shortening the sufferings which can often be just as much moral as physical. It is certainly not always easy to resist the urgent entreaties of friends. The least that can often be said of such entreaties is that their real motives escape us, and, in all cases, that they are wanting in light and in competence.

But it is the duty of a true doctor to use his authority to clarify and to remain sole master of his directions and his action, without being swayed by a blind sentimentality which knows nothing of higher and more enlightened charity. For a much greater reason, there can be no euthanasia or 'mercy-killing' for the Christian doctor; because life has been given or confided to us; it does not belong to us, neither our life nor the life of another. Let us wisely remain within the limits of our noble rôle, which is that of healing when we can; of soothing when cure eludes us; but all this without ever doing injury to the body or the soul. To deaden very keen suffering is always legitimate. It is for us to measure the intensity and the strength of the means at our disposal for doing so, because a good use can even, in certain circumstances, free the spirit from dominating and keen physical preoccupation, and by husbanding the sensibility which exhausts itself in over-intense suffering, can prolong life – which it is our rôle to do. Then, when all hope is lost, we must remind ourselves and our dying patients of that beautiful word of the Angel who will guide us in our new duties, when we take the measure of our professional impotence: 'Why do you seek Him who is living, among the dead?' Our concern is not, therefore, finished with those whom the wing of death is already touching. We must know how to conquer death by reminding ourselves that it is the entrance to a new life. It is important that this passage should not be made in ignorance, or in difference, or in rebellion. We have helped our patient in his suffering; we now help him to die, to die well, or more truly to be born again into eternal life.

There is no question, for the doctor, of sermons or long speeches. That is clearly not his rôle. Let him confine himself to a discreet admonition expressing his anxiety. For the most part, God will look to the rest, for this soul is more dear to Him than to ourselves. Who knows but that the peace of soul thus recovered may not even cause a new lease of life? What do we know of all the resources of a menaced organism? Because of our professional deformation, we do not take sufficient count of moral forces and of their influence over the physical. It partly rests with us, doctors, to create and to preserve among our patients this moral atmosphere, an element of peace for the efficacy of the forces of resistance. This is to strive for unity, the condition of equilibrium, in the human complex which we cannot fail to know.

It is difficult to give exact rules for the conduct of the doctor at the approach of death. They will depend on the circumstances, the milieu and the personal qualities of the doctor. But, speaking generally, it is a common fact that this approach of death occasions a certain anguish and disquiet in the patient. Without going beyond our rôle, and while keeping to the physical field which is ours, we can question our patients on the causes of this anguish, letting them know our concern to establish in them that peace which is indispensable to our therapeutic intervention. Following the form of our questions, they will very often take us into their confidence and, by avowing their physical and moral anxieties, they will give us the opportunity of advising them to place their trust in Providence, and from there we can lead them gradually into the way of peace and tranquillity of conscience.

We give this example, but we shall have occasion to suggest other means in the course of this exposition. We must put our mind at rest, in every way, against what might appear to be an indiscretion on our part; let us not forget that access to a very gravely ill person is very restricted. The doctor is the only one to whom all doors open, all restrictions are lifted, more readily even than to the priest or to the religious, even if the latter is a friend. This is a privilege which involves responsibilities for us. The patient is, for us doctors, our first neighbour always. Towards him, we have immediate and primary duties – those of a good Samaritan, of course; but our patients are not merely suffering and wounded bodies given into our care. We must not overlook the soul which assists the body in its fight, which informs it and which not only orientates its destiny but shares in that destiny.

If these circumstances are not compelling enough to calm our fears of being indiscreet, I shall go on to quote the Theologian, Rev. Father Tesson: 'The Doctor lays hold on the entire man, in the complexity of his tendencies, in the diversity of his elements. The position is certainly very difficult to maintain. But is it not the only one which is loyal and which fully respects things as they are?' I would even dare to say it is the only one which is logical. To ignore the soul of our patient is to be guilty of a fault of omission and a tactical error not only psychological but therapeutic. Even when the body seems condemned, there still remains before the eyes of Christian doctors an immortal soul, which we may not ignore or abandon. The way of the Christian doctor is not limited by time and by the present, like that of the unbeliever; it continues into eternity. It behoves the Christian doctor, therefore, not to interrupt the personal relationship which is the essence and the synthesis of the medical act. This contact cannot be limited to bodily preoccupations; it is a human relationship which ought to end by lifting itself to spiritual concerns, to the soul. To ignore the whole man in our patient is to fail in our mission; it is to remain an incomplete doctor, half way to our goal. The sick do not deceive themselves, who give their preference, their confidence and their fidelity to a complete doctor, to him who is known to act beyond the requirements of matter, to love and serve not only the bodies but the souls, not only the sick by healing them, but the dying by assisting them in death. If the 'personal relationship,' so well defined by Duhamel, is an act of man to man, it neither ought to be nor can be restricted to bodily preoccupations, the body being but part of man. It must extend to the spiritual domain, because it includes everything in man, corporal and spiritual, which makes him man.

On this condition, the contact gives satisfaction to both the body and soul of the man, or rather of the two men who are face to face. Let it not be said, from I know not what desire for neutrality – a neutrality which would be, humanly speaking, simply an abandonment and a deceit – that the doctor must keep to his therapeutic square, and that he is concerned with nothing beyond that square.

We could discuss at length the elements of a therapy which, to be complete, cannot ignore the psychical reactions of the organism. These dissenters, when faced with a miracle, do not fail to invoke the sole and sovereign, while still inexplicable, action of psychical forces to effect cures impossible of realisation by the sole action of natural forces. If the psychic element is so powerful, why should the doctor ignore it and refuse to call on its aid in his daily practice? Is it not his rôle to create the atmosphere most favourable to this therapeusis, by achieving in his patient, above all, the appeasement of all anxiety, of all unquiet, in the peace of a newly found soul? To contribute to this by our attitude, our advice and our authority, is to carry out our human rôle towards our patients. It is to soothe them while aiding them to die and to endure with renewed or increased moral strength when physical strength fails the pangs of the last agony.

The Truth

Christ said: 'I am the Truth.' There is, therefore, but one Truth of which we are in all circumstances the servants.

And what do we find most often about the sick, and with increased intensity as the condition of the patient gets worse? A real conspiracy of lies: pious lies, it is said, though they serve more often the prince of lies than the God of Truth.

What would we say of the duty of truth towards these sick? Is it not the beginning of charity not to deceive? Of course, charity excludes neither prudence nor delicacy. But the patient who has always relied on the sincerity of those about him; who, when in health, has never had reason to complain of their truth or of their solicitude – preserves the same attitude of confidence when he becomes a patient. He relies on his own in the hour of danger, and it is in that hour that they conspire to deceive him, to create for him the illusion of a security which no longer exists, and of a hope which is already beginning to fade. The first duty of the doctor is to reveal to those attending the patient and to the patient's relations the danger and the possibility of a fatal issue. This revelation is not meant to intensify the conspiracy of silence and of falsehood surrounding the patient, but to seek collaboration in preparing the patient to hear the truth.

Nothing is gained by delay. The more serious the patient's condition becomes, the more difficult it is to tell him.

His friends may find it too difficult to inform the patient, and so they may default. It then becomes possible for the doctor, as his duty demands of him, to act with that simplicity and in that manner which his heart dictates to him.

If we are really disturbed about the patient's condition, without our hope being shaken, it is best to act before all opportunity is lost. Let us bring this uneasiness of ours clearly to the attention of our patient, rather than dissimulate it under an appearance of reassuring and deceiving joviality. It is not necessary to shout this uneasiness, but we can allow our patient to divine it for himself.

The patient who has noticed our troubled expression as we examine him will question us. Let us not answer immediately, to give the impression that we are hesitating before a truth hard to hear. This deliberate silence will already be, for the still conscious patient, a warning of danger.

If the patient insists, before we leave him, let us admit our concern and specify the deterioration in his condition. This avowal on our part will make his way clear to him. From that moment, his attendants, duly and clearly informed, will create even all unconsciously about the patient this atmosphere of inquietude favourable to a more formal warning, which the patient already expects and is ready to meet without surprise and often with gratitude. At the next visit, the patient will watch our expression and, not finding there the relaxing of tension he hoped for, will perhaps demand the truth about his condition. To this request, dictated by his material concerns and by his spiritual, we have no right to answer with a lie. To lie at this moment is to be guilty, more than ever, of betrayal; because the consequences of our lie can be irreparable, both in the material and temporal domain, and in the spiritual domain for eternity.

These rules hold good in other, less dramatic circumstances which contain a sufficient element of uncertainty to justify words calculated to imply a warning. It should be given regularly when a surgical operation, even though not urgent, is indicated and the patient desires to be told clearly how grave the intervention will be, if there is any immediate danger involved. If this is serious and constitutes a risk which is real but indispensable to the conservation of life, our duty is to recognise it without exaggeration. The patient, who desires especially to set his material and spiritual house in order, has a right to the truth. The mildest of operations is not exempt from complications and can end by being fatal. Of course, it is not necessary to give these technical details of complications which happily are the exception; but to the question: 'This is not serious, is it, Doctor?' – we can always answer: 'Every operation is a serious matter and must be treated by both doctor and patient as a serious matter. It is best, in every case, to take all necessary material and spiritual precautions. That will be even technically the best psychical preparation for the operation.'

What is required of the unbelieving doctor in the material order, imposes itself with even greater force on the Christian doctor in the spiritual order. The two needs urge him in relation to his patients. I would say once more that there is in man – and especially for us doctors, there is very particularly in our patients – a 'demand that the whole man be considered.' Without committing an essential – I would venture to say *professional* – error, we cannot neglect in this totality the essential quality, which is its spirit, its soul. If one could doubt the necessity for

the doctor of a hierarchy which places the spiritual quality in the
foremost place, I would say that at the decisive hour when the
body yields and we feel that it is ready to dissolve, the soul
appears as stripped of its carnal vesture, more immediately, more
directly accessible to our charity, to our action. Its antennae are
more sensitive, ready to respond to even the most discreet invitation. Our duty to truth is not to let pass inactively that brief
instant when contact is possible, or better still, when contact is
easy because material chains are weakening and the soul frees
itself from a host of prejudices, human respects, contingencies.
The soul becomes more sensitive and sees better, in the confidence which it preserves in the doctor, the counsel which lifts it
up above carnal preoccupations to a perfect colloquy of soul
with soul.

Finally, the doctor is not by the sick-bed simply as a stranger,
as one who heals. When his therapeutic rôle seems completed,
with the approach of death, there remains the Christian soul
which he helps to die and to die happily.

Who knows whether, in the free choice which the patient made
of his doctor in a remote or recent past, he was not concerned to
choose him because he was 'Christian'? What does such a choice
mean if not that a part of the confidence which he had in the
doctor was accorded to him in view of the fact that he would act,
not only as a good doctor, but also as a Christian, in light and in
truth. And this is true not only in the sickness which is cured, but
even more in the sickness unto death. Hence our responsibility
as Christians is involved. Our patients rely on us, and we have
not the right to hide ourselves. The patient has called on us,
Christian doctors, for an assurance, a promise of truth, which we
must fulfil.

How are we to discharge this promise? By our professional
habits, which is to say precisely by what constitutes the function
of art in medicine, and by this art generously and diligently
exercised in the service of our patients. The doctor who is always
very busy, always inundated by his patients – or who finds it
useful for his reputation to appear so – will neglect to create
about his patient this atmosphere of trust, of confidence, of
friendship, which prepares the way for the truth. In a word, the

doctor ought to know how 'to waste his time' with his patient, which 'waste' will often be the means of gaining eternity. It will therefore be a remote preparation for an always possible death. Let us take care not to wait till the last moments, lest death should steal a march on our intentions. Even when there is no danger but merely a possible threat, we must know how to accustom our patients at times to hold intimate conversations with us which are not just concerned with material considerations of medicines and cures. Let us direct these moments of confidence towards what Pascal called 'the good usage of sickness.' In this terrain, the transition is easy to the quest for psychic equilibrium and peace of heart. Thus the chat veers more spontaneously towards the spiritual order, naturally inspired by this presence of God, at the approach of danger or of death. It behoves us Christian doctors to recognise this more active presence, to feel it, that we may make it known to our patients in the hour when the devil roams 'seeking whom he may devour.' The latter's weapon is very often, as we have been able to experience it in ourselves as well in others during illness, a kind of torpor in which the soul sinks and slumbers, like the Apostles in the Garden of Gethsemane. Now, the precept is a formal one: 'Watch and pray.' During lucid periods of health, one has taken wise and virile resolutions for the time of sickness. That time having come, one allows oneself to sink into an inertia which is almost without thought, which causes us to forget everything to the extent of neglecting the opportune moment which Providence gives for reconciliation. Instead of increasing that torpor of soul by torpor of the body, we must be on our guard in order to re-awaken, in these well-disposed souls, the resolutions so wisely taken before the time of trial for the time of trial. And when we shall have fulfilled this duty of truth and of charity towards our patients, it will still remain for us to pray in the hour of their agony.

The Life

Christ has said: 'I am the Life.' This word should vivify and enlighten our concept of Christian doctors at grips with death.

Let us recall that, in order to attain to true life in its fullness, it is necessary to pass through the portal of death. But this passage is difficult, encumbered by all the useless baggage of the life of this earth. It is also sad, because it means the breaking of all associations formed in the course of this life, with this after-taste of immortality which remains on the lips of all men since the Fall.

At the moment of this inevitable detachment it would seem that everything conspires about the dying person to hold him back. He is weighed down by material preoccupations which multiply for him. Even a patient who ought to be, by his milieu, his past and his Christian habits, the best prepared, is often absorbed by his entourage and the fact of his sickness, in cares, fatigue and suffering which turn his serious thoughts from death, from judgment and from his coming entry into eternal life.

It is, however, the solemn moment when God is present, when He comes before His creature with all His mercy and all His love. Let the doctor then be the ambassador of God to these souls. The patients will be grateful to us for it, because there will be a rest to prescriptions, to examinations, to that hard discipline of the sick of which they begin to feel more the weight than the benefit. For a life ends and another begins which demands other cares and other counsels.

We can be the first to detect this need and to confirm this call to the supernatural life.

If we have this good, friendly habit of a chat with our patients which has nothing to do with questions of temperature, of prescriptions or of diet, it will be easy for us to turn the conversation towards light and towards life. Let us study ways and means of letting those who tend the patient take part in these salutary conversations, so that gradually an atmosphere of light, of Truth and of Life may take the place of the conspiracy of silence and deceit.

If it is objected that such a dreadful truth would come as a dangerous shock, we should answer that our experience confirms the efficacy of this enlightenment, which rarely comes as a surprise and always calms. Very often, the silence and apparent indifference of our patients are the result of their concern not to alarm those about them. The doctor is very often aware of this misunderstanding and the patient may even confide it to him, so that it becomes easy for the doctor to dispel it in order to re-establish the harmony and understanding that should sweeten these last hours.

It is not for me, a doctor, to remind Christians that there is always actual grace, a grace of the present moment, and that it is as real, as assured for parents and relations, as it is for the doctor who takes this initiative, or as it is for the patient who is the subject of our solicitude.

The tranquil death which we desire for our patients as for ourselves is not necessarily the unconscious death which drugs, even prudently administered, can procure. We seek above all a peaceful death, with the soul at peace and abandoned to good-ness and mercy which opens to it the gates of eternal life. The sweetness of death is in that vision of light and of life.

When we watch the hour of death nearing those we love, as the mind darkens, the eyes lose their interior light, the speech becomes unintelligible, with what anguish do we not lean to-wards them to seek a last flicker of life, a final show of affection, a last word of farewell, which will remain as a spiritual testament among our most precious memories.

Do not let us change, by a useless and merely spectacular attempt at medical intervention, this last and precious contact between the living, and this final possibility of colloquy with God on which eternity may depend.

Even in the case of those farthest from God, we like to think and to believe that Mercy offers to the soul an opportunity of greeting It or repulsing It, in the last flicker of intelligence and of liberty. Shall we, by a gesture aimed at the entourage rather than the patient and which does not even hide our human medical impotence, shall we run the risk of standing in the light of this last vision of God, and thus preventing an adherence which often remains, in spite of appearances, the supreme hope of the survivors and the assurance of a happy eternity for the patient?

In the apprehension of these serious realities, let us, on the contrary, pursue to the end our true rôle as doctors – our rôle of respect for life – towards all and in spite of all. Let us even attempt, against all hope and all human evidence, to gain the second which will decide the destiny of the soul confided to us in the suffering body. Let us remind ourselves that death deprives man of possibilities, that it closes the account of good and evil, but that it leaves the judgment and the debt, as we said at the beginning of this exposition. Finally, let us console ourselves for our impotence in face of death by telling ourselves that to save a soul is really to conquer Death, since it assures Life with Him who is the Life.

Let us remain faithful to Him, in His Way, His Truth and His Life!

J. OKINCZYC
Professeur agrégé à la Faculté de Paris
Chirurgien honoraire des Hôpitaux de Paris

DEATH, THE TEST OF LOVE AND THE CONDITION OF LIBERTY

However enormously diversified may be the course of human lives, all without exception begin through birth and end in death. But I bear not the slightest responsibility for my birth, and I carry no memory of it. The temporal, local, racial, family and other circumstances of my birth have greatly influenced the whole course of my destiny, but it was entirely independent of me. Whether under a blessing or a curse, my birth took place and I could not shape its pattern. It is eternally what it has been, for it belongs to the past.

It is entirely otherwise with my death. It lies inescapably before me, but it has not yet come. It *will be*, and I may therefore expect it and prepare for it. My liberty, which could not intervene in my birth, can now exercise itself, in this at least, that I may at this moment bring about my own death, if I so wish. Suicide is a permanent possibility with man, and it often suggests itself when life turns sour. Correlatively, the preservation of life can be regarded as the result of a progressive acceptance.

In fact, however, rather than consent to life or refuse it, many attach themselves to it with a frenzy that is full of anguish and wilful blindness. We fear death, and we use all our strength to forget it. 'I too shall die'; and meantime there is no species of 'diversion,' ennobling or vulgar, which we have not invented to dim the radiance of that evident truth. Avoiding what reminds us of it, we cultivate the habit of thinking always of death as of something that concerns others, only *others*, and we live more or less as the fools of our own blind faith. But in this domain as in all others, repression and insincerity profoundly disturb conscience and life. The world at large sees us as people immensely sure of ourselves, for that is the face we show; but secretly we are ceaselessly measuring how near the abyss has come towards us, and we find ourselves – sometimes more, sometimes less – aghast at the thought of it. Instead of lying to ourselves, instead of playing our part in the comedy or tragi-comedy, would it not be more simple, more courageous, more human, to meditate serenely on the mystery of death – my death?

Yes, but how are we to get light on our subject? My death is absolutely certain, but its modalities are wrapped in uncertainty and it has this unique character of being completely 'inexperienceable.' Those who break the seal of its secret do not return to tell us either how the trial is offered, or how they have met it, or how we in our turn must face up to it. Being strictly personal, death is an act in which the experience of others can give us but very feeble help. On the other hand, whoever is willing to 'contemplate' death, in order to discover its significance, can do so only by integrating it in a metaphysical or religious world-outlook in which it will constitute an integral element of the whole. For all that, a concrete philosophy must explore all ways, and collect all the indications which, in different degrees, bring us nearer to the heart of the mystery. We wish to point out some of them.

I

The greatest fear with which death shadows us, a fear which comes alive in us every time we see a dear one depart from us, is the fear of *separation*. A far-reaching enquiry into all the forms of pleasure, of satisfaction, of happiness and of joy would show that, in spite of apparent and explicable failures, the element of beatitude resides always in the birth or the deepening of a union, while separation, on the contrary, always connotes suffering, pain, misfortune, sorrow. However one may explain it, death remains a rupture of a certain mode of union with the world, with beloved persons, with his own body. For this reason, it will be always painful. Christ was not ashamed to weep before the tomb of Lazarus. But sorrow will differ immensely from sorrow, according to whether the mode of union broken by death will be considered concretely as the only mode which man can know, or as a particular mode subordinated to other modes of union.

In the first case, death is a final misfortune, without issue or remedy. It is complete annihilation. I identified myself with my riches, with my possessions, with my *having*, and I *shall have* nothing any more, which in this hypothesis means: I *shall be* nothing any more. I loved the body above all, and love seldom and with difficulty left the plane of sexual relations and sensible caresses; now that the body lies there, ready to be bound in its sere-cloth and put in the clay, I have nothing left of myself. A woman throws herself like a maniac on the corpse of her lover, clings to it, howls her animal despair. No, nothing will remain of possessions, of caresses, and for those who have known no other joys here below, death comes as an absolute end, as a thing evil in itself.'

But if the love is spiritualised; if it reaches the plane of friendship; if the objective fact of *being there* and of outwardly manifesting one's presence – however precious this may be – is subordinated entirely or almost entirely to the intangible, indescribable fact of *being with*, of fusing *our* existence in a common destiny, of being *us* rather than two juxtaposed *egos*, of being *together*, open to all love rather than imprisoned in separate cocoons of egoism – then the wrench of death, though it tears and pains, will not reach the depths of this love, of this friendship. As the *Lettres à l'absent* of Mireille Dupouey or the *Liens immortels* of Alice Ollé-Laprune bear witness, among others, the experience of a communion which lives on after the death of one of the partners is far from rare among Christian people. Death, this time, far from being experienced as a final absence, shows rather that I reach the beloved person more intimately than I could know and above all express. The disappearance of the apparent interpreters of our love shows me, as the cloudless fidelity at times of temporary separation has already indicated, that our reciprocal presence can dispense with external signs without being really altered.

After the first stupefaction and wave of sorrow which follows the death of a spouse, a child, a dearly loved father or mother, a friend, there are many who sometimes feel, from the moment when they recollect themselves beside the bed of state, that the dear one is still very near to them, no longer in this laid-out body, but *with them* through the inner language of the heart. The keeping of communion with the departed now rests with the one who survives. If I say that he no longer exists, or at least that I can have no further intimacy with him, he no longer holds anything for me, since I have, in effect, freely consummated his death, so that for me he is now annihilated. But so far from considering his memory as a lifeless and silent relic, I am inspired by his spirit, I keep myself in his brilliance, I consult him in the depths of my heart, he does not die for me. Sheer illusion, will be the answer of all spirits fed on positivism. Experience, however, would have its word to say, but it is clear that the very postulate of rationalism forbids its devotee to have recourse to this kind of experience. We enter, in fact, into an order of things where, on a very sure objective base, *reality* nevertheless depends on our liberty. Is it not always so, when love intervenes? Without my having a hand in it, the *other person* certainly exists and I too *exist* but without him; but that we two should form a united home, a couple of friends, depends on our own free will. The *being* of our communion is really *created* by the oath – explicit in marriage, most often implicit in friendship – which links us one to the other.

It is for our fidelity to perpetuate this *being*, even beyond the hazard of death. Our treason alone can annihilate it. He is numbered among those friends to whom I feel myself nearer than to others who are separated from me by life alone or with whom I even rub shoulders daily, in that the dead, because they are dead, can exercise a more profound *actual* influence over me. I need only to recollect myself in order to find them again such as they were and infinitely better, so understanding and so good that before them every mask, all duplicity, falls away, and we live together in an intimacy unknown in this world where our bodies separate us from one another. Love and friendship, says the proverb, are stronger than death. For those who have had experience of it, the wound which the death of a dear one causes does not harbour that incurable poison which envenoms the existence of those whose life is bounded by the tangible. Death is faced up to with serenity because there is a sure hope that it will not sever all relations. He who can say with St. Thérèse of the Child Jesus: 'I shall pass my heaven in doing good on earth,' will not look on death as a hopeless rupture, and it will cease to be the greatest of all suffering.

Inasmuch as the real love in which I participate already here on earth can reach its fullness only in the after-life, I can legitimately long for death, not as for itself but because it conditions this full union. 'I wish to be dissolved *that I may be* with Christ' (St. Paul); 'Come, Lord Jesus, do not tarry' (St. John); 'Je me meurs de ne pas mourir' – 'I die because I cannot die' (St. Teresa of Avila). The same invocation ceaselessly echoes through the Christian centuries. 'There is a man,' says Lacordaire, 'whose love is ever mindful of the tomb.' Although we have not that familiar contact with Him which the disciples enjoyed, Jesus remains present among us. It is to Him that the amity, the fidelity is directed which faces up to death and to the disappearance of the bodily presence. He Himself foresaw it when He said to His apostles: 'I tell you the truth, it is good for you that I go. For if I go not, the Paraclete will not come to you.' Spiritual presence infinitely surpasses mere visible presence.

Such desires for death are certainly rare where only love intervenes. Very often, as my friend André Godin has established, they correspond to a process of disengagement which denotes rather a diminution or a deviation of affectivity. It would be a gross illusion to attribute the least mystical value to declarations which reflect merely discouragement or egoistical frustration. Finally one sees that with authentic saints, the love of Christ can be so intense that, without doing anything to hasten the moment of their death, they await it with trembling joy.

How far removed we are, in their case, from the initial horror which constitutes our lot! Death rises up as a criterion of our affections. How my reaction to it differs according to whether my attachment is made heavy with the flesh or lifted to the spirit! Death is the great test of love.

II

But is not fidelity beyond the tomb an illusion? In reality, does the departed one still live, whether he lives *for me* or not? This is a crucial question to which, at all times, the spontaneous faith of humanity, such as the religions and nearly all the systems of metaphysics have expressed it, has answered in the affirmative. One postulate only, it must be remarked, valid for certain special disciplines, entails the negative. This postulate is adopted and unduly extended by those who cannot or do not wish to preserve that friendship with the dead of which we have spoken. In this relation of fidelity, 'experience' (if we may be permitted to use this ambiguous word) recognises the other person, not at all as the figment of an over-heated imagination, but as real, as active. And, experience weighed against experience, it is clear that we have no proof of annihilation – how could we have? – while a myriad of accounts among all peoples maintain the belief in immortality and claim to relate communications of interventions from beyond the grave.

Nearly two thousand years ago, a Man died, nailed naked to the gibbet of a slave, after unspeakable physical and moral sufferings. In order to assure himself, though assurance was not needed, that the Man was dead, a Roman soldier pierced His heart. With this Man, died the hope of a little group of friends who had hailed the Messiah in Him – the Saviour of the world. All this came to a sad end on the evening of Good Friday. All His companions had forsaken Him on the evening before, when the soldiers had taken Him. The chief of His Apostles had denied Him with an oath: 'I know not the man.' It was another of His friends who had sold Him for thirty pieces of silver! Now that He is dead, nothing remains of His work.

A few days later, however, see how this work came alive again and, after two very chequered milleniums, continues more vigorous than ever: the Catholic Church.

The origin of this new life is the irrefutable, triumphant faith in the certain resurrection of Christ. It was certainly not lightly admitted. No one, it is clear, expected it – not after such a death! Certain disciples, whom He rejoined on the road, were sadly discussing their dead hopes, even while some women were announcing the visitation of angels and the apostles were establishing the disappearance of His body. The empty sepulchre was not enough to convince them. They must see Him, hear Him, eat with Him, feel Him, in order that their doubts may be dispersed. But then, these poor men who had fled at the approach of a danger which did not threaten them are to become vessels of strength. They will overcome all sufferings. They will accept martyrdom to bear witness that He, Jesus, has conquered death and that they have seen Him living beyond the tomb!

They now remember that He had announced this glorious life to them, at a time when they were not yet able to understand what He meant; they see how this new life threads itself through the woof of His existence and of His message; they know that it is the promise of our own resurrection. And in spite of the innumerable faults and failures of those who people and direct her, the Church carries through the centuries the fidelity of her origin, and lives in the Presence of her living Head, risen from the dead.

This fact, established by tradition, by documents and by the formidable consequences which still continue into our own days, cannot be denied for purely historical reasons, because no event in history rests on more solid proofs. Without entering into the discussion of Apologetics on the subject of the Person of Christ, we shall rely, in order to elucidate the mystery of which we are treating, on the lessons to be drawn from this fact: a man has conquered death. Now, anguish grips us when we ask ourselves whether the deceased opens a door on another life, or steps into the void. Through the example of Christ we know that death is a path, not an ending.

Even after the resurrection of Christ, however, the characteristics of the life beyond the tomb did not abundantly appear – and undoubtedly the mystery must remain an essential condition of the trial which death provides. At least let us ascertain what we can learn about it.

Unique in His theandric personality, Christ remains our prototype, the 'first-born among the dead,' especially with regard to the life of glory. While remembering that He differs from us in that He is Head of the Church of which we are members, we can legitimately infer our own resurrection from His.

It is incontestable that during his entire earthly existence, man is very limited in his freedom. We say that he becomes free. Progressively he disengaged himself from hereditary, family, social, etc., factors of determination, which he accepts or combats; he orientates himself as best he can among dark forces, and he attempts, if he really wishes to free himself, to draw the best from them for his personal ends. But how far removed is this precarious liberty from the divine liberty in the image of which it is, however, created!

In spite of the infinite distance which separates it from its model, it tends nevertheless to resemble that model. Is not the rhythm of human existence determined by an increased progressive possibility of the realisation of self? Grafted at first in some sort on the life of another – that of the mother – grafted too by an act in which it does not participate in any way, since it did not exist before this conception, the embryo gradually puts forth movements which are independent of the maternal influx. Birth breaks the primitive symbiosis, and projects it into an existence which is biologically autonomous but still utterly dependent. The child has chosen neither race, nor family, nor place, nor date of his birth; he has not chosen his fatherland, his social milieu, language, rules of etiquette, aesthetic criteria, the moral principles and religious practice which education brings him, physical temperament, character – in fact, nothing; he has not even chosen to exist. But flung into the adventure of life, he must gradually take it up on his own account, abandon, bend, modify all the 'given' elements which characterise him. On the biological plane, as on the intellectual, moral, social, religious, he gradually acquires his autonomy by a series of weanings, of crises, and of undertakings, and he chooses the attitude which will define him.

This passage from the 'imposed' to the 'personal' is especially evident at the period of puberty. The child is, in general, balanced, reasonable; he resembles more the adult than the adolescent. In full crisis, the latter calls everything in question. We can certainly admire in him the charm of promise and of generous impulses, but it must be recognised that there is nearly always a disproportion between his body and his imagination, his intelligence and his affectivity. The grace of childhood has disappeared with its equilibrium. But if the crisis resolves itself properly, is there anything more beautiful than the young man and the young woman in the harmonious development of a healthy body, a cultivated spirit, a solid moral life? The difference and the progress consist in the fact that the equilibrium of the child is *received*, is passive, is fixed by ignorance and immunity, while the adult, if he emerges victor from the crisis of puberty, has an active equilibrium which he has himself, at least partly, re-conquered.

At the age of vocation and choice of a career, he himself more or less decides the orientation of his life; he actively participates in the creation of his being. It rests with him, during the crisis of 25 to 30 years, to maintain his ideal while adapting it concretely to the hard conditions of real life of which the ardent enthusiasm of adolescence is often unaware. When he reaches maturity, it is less his origin and extrinsic circumstances which define his being than his personal value, his line of action, the family and the work he has founded.

Nevertheless, however profoundly he may correct himself, he works only on *given* foundations: his body with its possibilities and its blemishes, his character, his condition of life, the contingent state of the world at that moment. To be really 'the son of his works,' the son of his will and of his liberty – in short, to *posit* himself – a man would need to be able to give to himself a body fitted to himself and so formed as to determine the relations he will enter into with others exactly according to his wishes. The abandoning of the received body would therefore be an indispensable condition of auto-position in being, of full liberty. Now, is it not just this abandoning which appears most clearly in every death? As the butterfly abandons the cocoon where it has developed during its period of chrysalis, so too when we reach the definitive stage of our being, we leave aside the body which was the first and indispensable condition of our growth to spiritual maturity. The body which is mine during the process of 'becoming' is, in some sort, only the womb where is being formed, the 'being' which I shall be, my spirit made flesh. Indispensable during embryonic life, the rôle of the womb ceases at the moment of birth; thus, this body which I have not chosen, and which I cannot dispense with during my period of *becoming*, will disappear to give a place to my *being*. Thus we see that Christ keeps in His glorified body the stigmata of the Passion, the wound in His side and the marks of the nails in His hands and feet, without being content to revive the bloodless, torn and disfigured appearances of the body which was laid in the sepulchre.

What is true of my relation to my body, will not the same be true of all the other relations which define my being? At the moment of death, all is called in question (much more radically than at the period of puberty) and I have myself to choose my definitive attitude towards the universe, towards others, towards myself and towards God. Here on earth, I become master of this attitude in proportion as I attain to spiritual autonomy. Without changing in any way the *seity* of other beings, it depends on me whether God *for me* is real or inexistent – according to which attitude I shall live as a religious man or as an atheist. It depends on me whether I regard my fellow-beings as brothers or as strangers, according to which I either engage myself *with* them in the adventure of existence or play my game all alone with a somewhat disdainful air. It depends on me whether the universe has a magnificent meaning in serving towards our own divination, or becomes for me absurd, nauseating, heavy with despair – according to which attitude I either unite myself to it in enthusiastic offering and joyful service or I sever every relation which does not get its meaning from cold scientific knowledge or from possessive egoism. It rests with me whether I shall construct a sincere, affectionate, creative personality or whether I shall become desiccated in barren 'enlightenment' and wanton destruction – according to which attitude I shall return to my beginnings in fruitful meditation or I shall disperse myself in introspection and dissipation.

But here on earth, it must be realised, I can demonstrate only a certain orientation: I *am becoming* free, I *am not* yet free in the full sense of the word. My earthly choices seem to be, above all, preparatory exercises, 'repetitions' (as one repeats a passage or a studied discourse) of the definitive choice; they foster the birth of my liberty. Let us lift again to the spiritual plane the biological comparison from embryonic life. In his pre-natal existence, the child learns practically all the acts which will be indispensable to him on the day of his birth; his heart acquires a proper rhythm, he moves head, arms and legs, he even absorbs and digests what he can. Similarly, if we may be permitted the expression, we are here on earth as 'embryos of the spirit.' In the course of our earthly 'becoming,' we exercise ourselves to posit the definitive act; and this, whatever may be the duration and the exterior or interior conditions of our human existence. The progressive initiation of life, and the sudden revelation which crowns it in death, have scarcely anything in common. If the child could remember, he would tell us of the abyss which separated his life in the maternal womb from the existence into which birth has projected him, and how little the first, even while preparing for it, allowed any forecasting of the second. Now, there is not one among us who could ever instruct children still in gestation, concerning the experience of birth through which we have all passed. Without running the parallel too far and thus making it ridiculous, can we not say that our earthly existence is, from the viewpoint of our *spiritual being*, what pre-natal existence was for our *becoming*? Death, according to the beautiful expression of the old martyrologies, is the *dies natalis*, the day of authentic birth when, this time, I shall myself choose what I wish to be for eternity. That is why even our deceased friends allow the veil of mystery to cover the experience of 'dying.' The Platonic formula: 'Life, the apprenticeship for death' – acquires in this perspective a profound significance. The capital act of our earthly existence is indeed that which ends it – that in which becoming ceases in order to give place to *being*. Such is the act of dying.

An act, certainly. The person who watches a death agony would be inclined to consider death rather as a passivity, a decay. This is so because he sees only the end of a *becoming*, the failure of a transitory body which, its rôle completed, effectively weakens into decay. But this sad spectacle is but the reverse of reality. Breaking the chain which subjected it to a world of determination and constraint, the real being escapes to choose freely the relations which will constitute it. On a foundation of existence which my liberty can neither annihilate nor create (the *realitas-in-se* of God, of others, of the world, of myself), it rests with me to create their *reality for me*, my *being with them* or *without them*, communion or isolation, friendship or hatred. And what counts for me, my *being*, as distinct from my brute *existence*, is precisely this freely chosen attitude. We must not, however, go the length of imagining a creation '*ex nihilo*' by an isolated being. With us, the act of liberty essentially *answers* an invitation. The artist creates only as he is solicited by the beauty of the world or by inspiration. In the same way, I create myself as a free 'person' only in meeting another, only in corresponding with the grace of God.

But it is *I* who make this answer, and it can be a refusal or an acceptance – a refusal more or less radical, an acceptance more or less generous. Also, an infinite diversity will be found among the beings, each one choosing himself in an original, unpredictable, inimitable manner.

If we wished to introduce a hierarchy into this diversity, it would be necessary, in theological terms, to admit an infinity of 'degrees' between the highest in Heaven and the lowest in Hell. It is with this, indeed, that we are concerned. The choice posited in the act of dying is *per se* definitive, immutable. Eternity, it is well known, has nothing in common with time; it cannot be thought of as a very long time nor as an instant. Every time we succeed – if we ever do so here below – in seizing on totality as such (in poets, love or mystical ecstasy, for instance) eternity becomes a reality in us. But we return, alas, to temporality; apprehending only in part things in themselves particular, we are obliged to multiply our imperfect apprehensions, and this 'discourse' is at the root of our temporal 'becoming.' But in the act of dying, we shall have to invent our mode of immediate participation in the totality of existing beings. The choice made, in full light, there will be no reason for us or no possibility of calling it in question. Moreover, each of us will be, for eternity, exactly what he wishes to be. God has placed this in the power of man's own counsel. Each will behave according to his own good pleasure, and no one will regret his choice. Regret would suppose a second moment in relation to choice. But if a second moment were possible, why not also a third moment for a new choice, a fourth for a new regret, etc.? Eternity would no longer be immediate participation in the totality of the real, but a simple prolongation of the inconstancy of *becoming*, a period of experiences and of renewals.

Each one being exactly as he wishes to be, no one will regret his choice. Still, this does not mean that all will participate equally in beatitude. As we have briefly indicated at the beginning of this study, happiness is measured by union, suffering by rupture. Consequently, the highest degree of Heaven (we use evidently inadequate spatial configuration) – will be that in which the being wills itself wholly *with* the others, in a communion of love with all reality. The lowest depth of Hell will be that in which the being, centred on himself in isolation, will wholly exclude the others and wish himself *without* them.

With or *without* – the alternative between these two propositions summarises the whole matter. A choice between these two attitudes is at the heart of all our free actions, and the attitude gives the action its character. The metaphysicians will say, of course, that liberty does not necessarily imply choice. We admit that this is so in the case of infinite being. But limited being will always have to choose between that in which he participates with all the others, and the limit to which it is lawful to shut himself within himself. The distinction between the 'closed' and the 'open' rules all moral and religious order, where it defines the two contradictory poles of egoism and charity.

At the moment of dying, the *being* takes his measure. He chooses his degree of intimacy with the others (God, the world of spirits, the entire universe), or on the contrary his centring on self which seems preferable to him. He adopts for eternity the attitude which pleases him. It is in this plenary significance that the aphorism must be understood: 'All men are equal when faced with death.' This is so not only because all pass through the same trial, but above all because no one among them is set at a disadvantage by the circumstances imposed by his terrestrial *becoming*. The materiality of acts or the merits 'acquired' (as a treasure) will scarcely count at this moment. The fundamental orientation of the soul towards communion or towards isolation, will alone have significance. Every man, whatever his state in life, his heredity or the conditions of his existence, has gradually adopted this orientation for himself.

Everything is called in question at death, and the sudden revelation does not prolong homogeneously the progressive initiation; whence it follows, therefore, that the acts or at the very least the attitudes of our life do not in any way diminish in value. Experience, in its many positive and negative forms, educates our liberty. Sin – which always coincides with an egoistic or conceited centring on self – can, through the disgust which it inspires, open to communion, just as the normal development of the virtuous life does. But the latter is an infinitely better way – on condition, let it be well understood, that it is not vitiated by pharisaism which is also a form of self-conceit. The person orientated towards charity, who all his life has sought a more profound union with God and with others, will open with fully spontaneity the moment this communion is proposed to him. Scarcely any hesitation is possible about the eternal destiny of a genuinely charitable man; and the Church, which forbids any statement that any particular soul is damned, lists countless saints whose beatitude it certifies.

It is for the soul centred on itself that the final choice will have an especially tragic character. In acceding to the final plane of being, it is absolutely possible for a soul to be completely converted. But this *volte-face* will be all the more difficult – because of ingrained habits – as the egoism is more inveterate. And this exactly proportioned difficulty constitutes the Christian 'Purgatory' – in which hypothesis, this latter need not necessarily be considered under a temporal mode. Finally, it can happen that, in spite of the entirely new conditions of choice, the completed and egoistic person remains obstinate in refusing charity, and elects to be separated for eternity in hell.

Have we not the shadow of the experience of this choice and of this double possibility, in the profound reaction which the belief that death is very near provokes in us? The imminence of danger frees us from our attachments, and occasions at the same time a strong release of affectivity. Now, very often, one of two phenomena is noticed in the person thus roused: either a conversion from mediocrity to a better life, or on the contrary an exacerbation of wanton egoism. The intrusion of the absolute into human life consecrates and fixes the generally accepted orientation rather than overthrows it. The *Sparkenbroke* of Morgan, if he remains for ever marked by the precocious experience which he has in the family crypt, will become neither more altruistic nor more religious. On the contrary, the *Annick* whose story Jacqueline Vincent tells us in *Comme par mégarde* will achieve a fundamental generosity only on the threshold of death. Far from literary allusions, on the plane of daily existence, have we not all met with people, some of whom give to charity all that they consider to be surplus to precarious living, while others rush forward with increased frenzy to pleasure and ambitious competition? The thought of death alone acts like a catalysis and forces us to take up a position. Hence meditation on death is always imposed in ascetics, and will always find its normal place in the conduct of a retreat. Death calls forth liberty, and reveals the depths of hearts.

The two themes developed rejoin. Death is at once the test of love and the condition of liberty, because liberty has no other deep significance than that it permits love. The Divine Trinity who created us invites us to participate in His intimate life which is the communion of Charity between the Three Divine Persons. *Invites us;* for of what interest to God would be the person who would not have accepted freely and chosen freely to love Him – a person, therefore, who would not have freely overcome the temptation to refuse or to betray? This helps us to understand the meaning of our creation.

Every man is born here into a *community* which imposes itself on him as a fact anterior to his free will. But the more he becomes aware of his personal autonomy, the more it rests with him either to sever the relations which would unite him with others, or, on the contrary, to accept and deepen them. According to his choice, he will either imprison himself in the *isolation* of egoism or pride, he will live *without* others, or he will open himself to communion with God and with men, whom he goes out of himself to meet in faith and in love. Just as in the order of knowledge, we begin with a rich but confused primitive *complex*, the *analysis* of which gives elements which re-group to form the *synthesis*, so too the dialectic of love is completed in the order of love only when, disengaged from the imposed *community*, we freely accede to communion. But to speak of liberty is to imply the possibility of branching off on the way. Just as the analysis is indispensable in order to pass from the confusion of the complex to the harmony of the synthesis, but implies the danger of falling short (as is the case with highly scientific but one-tracked minds) and failing with both the complex and the synthesis, so liberty alone permits the passage from community to communion, but implies the risks of individualist isolation which tears from the community without introducing into the communion.

Whoever, then, wishes his life to be a success will aspire simultaneously to the highest liberty and will orientate firmly that liberty in the direction of charity. Only on that condition will death lose for him its sinister character of absolute rupture. It has often been noticed that the primitive or the little child accepts death with much greater ease than do the majority of civilised adults. This is because the child and the primitive are scarcely free from the community. The strictly personal problem of their destiny and their survival troubles them very little. But it is especially the highly civilised person resting at an intermediate stage between community and communion, who is racked with anguish. 'Disintegrated,' as the sociologists say, uprooted from the group into which he was born, he has not yet engaged in a new union, he has not yet fashioned anew a superior set of surroundings where he can open himself to love. And when, in addition, he has chosen isolation, death must seem to him the worst of catastrophes, because it seems to threaten the annihilation of that *ego* to which alone he grapples his being. On the contrary, we have seen when reading the witness of the saints that those who lift themselves to authentic communion have no fear of death. Death will merely change the form of their love; it will not destroy anything.

The fanaticism of certain young Nazis who flung themselves into the carnage, in the intoxication of the first battles of 1940, resulted in their being integrated in the community. One cannot help being reminded of those animals who sacrifice themselves for the good of the species. Such a death is unworthy of man.

But the attitude of the deserter through egoism is scarcely better. Without a care for other or for superior interests at stake in the conflict, he thinks only of his own well-being. If he uses his liberty, it is directed towards isolation. And again it is he who, unable to endure the wounds of life, will commit suicide when the disillusionment becomes too raw, when life – from his individual point of view – 'is no longer worth the trouble of being lived.'

The Christian, on the contrary, knows that, according to the word and the example of Christ, there is no greater love than to give one's life for those one loves, but to give it oneself, freely, through love.

Submission to death through instinct, refusal of death through selflove, suicide dictated by egoism, are all crimes. But when generously accepted, death brings the supreme completion to him who inclines himself towards charity. If one wishes to measure the chasm which separates the community which precedes or excludes personal liberty from the communion which follows and crowns it, one should weigh the difference that exists between the gregarious madness of death for the race, and the sacrifice of his life offered by the soldier who exposes himself to danger to save a companion or to fulfil a mission. But when the community denies liberty, voluntary isolation perverts it and this is a much more serious matter. Hence is justified the general reprobation which brands the deserter or the suicide. (Still, the act of suicide, even when followed immediately by death, is only the second last act of existence, the last being that of dying which can radically transform the moral orientation).

In every hypothesis, the most human and the most Christian attitude towards life, and in the perspective of death, is the progressive opening up to the totality of the real, the apprenticeship of ever increasing intimacy with God, with others, with the deep self and with the universe. And when, in charity, we shall participate profoundly in all that is, we shall, like Francis of Assisi, finish our canticle of the creatures with praise of our sister Death.

'Laudate sii, mi Signore, per sora nostra morte corporale de la quale nulu omo vinente po'scampare.

'Guai a quilli che morrano in le peccata mortali.

'Beati quilli che si trovarano in le tue santissime voluntati, ca la morte secunda non li potera far mal.'

O day of the Encounter, I await you in peace because I trust in Thy immense Goodness, O Lord.

R. TROISFONTAINES

THE PRIEST AT THE BED-SIDE
OF THE DYING

There are two men who, by their functions, meet together because they both work on a common subject, the most affecting of all subjects: *Man*.

The subject is not man as he is revealed in his ordinary and exterior relations, but man considered in what constitutes the most intimate part of his being; in the very sources of his life, the sources of his physical life, as well as the sources of his moral and spiritual life. The subject is, therefore, man made more true to himself by the imminence of death which leads him to recognise himself for what he really is, now that the temporary part of his being, which he has so long considered as permanent, is slipping from him and beginning to disintegrate. And what is perhaps more affecting still is that these two men who meet to labour for such a man will themselves one day be that man.

Thus the exercise of their profession leads them to see themselves also in what constitutes their most intimate and true nature, to remove the masks and the appearances, and – if they wish to go the root of the exigencies of what they shall have recognised – to be no longer capable of exercising their profession except by giving themselves wholly to it.

These two men are the doctor and the priest, both labouring for the man who is today the patient, tomorrow the dying man, the day following the lifeless being, cold in death.

We do not say of this man that he is man eternal, unless we indicate by the word the man of all time, or all conditions, of every latitude. We say of him that he is simply *man*, man in what makes him a man.

What investigation into man will these two men have to make?

It will be more than an ordinary exploration where it suffices to discover the characteristic traits of an earthly region, because here it is a living, mysterious, disturbed country where the explorer, at every step he advances, must call on all the resources of his profession. He seeks to explore, to discover, in order that he may heal; he seeks to enlighten in order that he may awaken the last forces of life.

A first serious reconnaissance of the field reveals the error of an oversimplified and perhaps current view: to the doctor pertain the sources of physical life in the man; to the priest, the sources of spiritual life.

In traditional terms, the one concerns himself with the body, the other with the soul, and they follow each other or precede each other; if they meet together, it is not for any consultation, but to arrange the order of precedence. They have nothing in common.

This is a pure fiction, because the two sources are inseparable one from the other. If they have a different origin, they are united until death, and only death can sever their union. It is not *any* living body, as if it were that of an animal, which the doctor must attend; it is a human body. It is not a pure spirit with which the priest must deal, but the spirit of a man which exercises itself, which expresses itself through his body.

These two sources converge in one story – the story of man, a story traced in his body, traced in man, but which has only one subject – the famous *reed* of Pascal.[1]

A *reed* which is destructible, at grips with the universe; a *thinking reed* which cannot reach the universe because it does not belong to it and escapes from it. A *reed* which affirms its immortality in the instant when it knows it is dying and knows why it dies.

It is with this splendid reality of the whole man that these two men, the doctor and the priest, are concerned as by their functions. They can understand this reality only if they accept it such as it is, in its full extent, in all its depth – a depth which will never be sounded, because to sound it would require the power to reach back to the sources of life in its first springing, and therefore to the secret of God. It would also be to penetrate the story of this life which writes itself beside that one in the body as well as in the soul.

1. This is a reference to a famous passage in the *Pensées* which begins: 'Man is as reed the most feeble thing in nature, but he is a thinking reed.' (Translator's note.)

It is not immaterial to their approach to this mysterious reality that the doctor and the priest should bear in mind what they are in themselves, independently of their function. This function will be all the more assured if the initial contact is a simple and true human contact and not just a professional one.

It is important that each should be profoundly human in his conduct, in his greeting, in his words, in his delicate appreciation of the mystery which the person dealt with bears in himself, whether that person is sick or dying. His attitude will depend on the attitude of priest or doctor, so closely is his attention fixed on each.

This is an attitude which expresses the true function of the doctor and the priest. For, beyond the special elements whose importance cannot of course be denied, they must seek in the patient him whom we would call eternal man, man stripped of his rank, of his profession, of his relations, of all the conventional things which might tend to falsify him in his relations with himself and with others.

All this pomp and circumstance which is so jealously guarded in ordinary life falls away in the doctor's consulting-room, but can still prove an obstacle to the priest.

We attain there to one of the summits which can orientate the life of a doctor or of a priest.

The doctor who knows the meaning of man and is not limited merely to the knowledge of his medical art, of the malady he treats, and of the patient he regards as a mere case, to whom, moreover, the patient volunteers information and is ready to entrust himself – can exercise a sacred function approximating to that of the priest.

In the body, he reads the sometimes lamentable history of a life; in the wound, he reads the end. He does not run the risk of meeting the prejudice which the priest encounters.

What confidence he can collect, what counsels he can give, what intimacies he can stir up in a patient who has opened himself to him, who has confidence in him because in him he has met a human spirit, a human heart which inclines to him to help him to rise.

The doctor who really knows the meaning of man can give back to a man who has lost it the meaning of his moral life, if not in a clear fashion, at least in the awakening of a conscience until then distracted or clouded. It is not our province to study the discipline which imposes on the doctor such a conception of his life as a doctor, and the culture which it demands; let it suffice for us to indicate the grandeur which it will confer on his personal life and the splendour to which that life will attain.

The same holds good for the priest, but his ways are more difficult.

The sick and the dying desire the doctor, because they expect from him victory over the sickness which is strangling them. They do not always show the same desire for the priest. Is this the case with many of them, and do they recognise only the sickness they carry within them, no longer in their body but in their soul? If they no longer appreciate the meaning of their soul; if their appreciation of the moral life is obscured in them; if the grip of their sufferings and of their physical lassitude centres them on their body so as to become almost absorbed in it – access to them is difficult.

Even more than the doctor, the priest, through a deep human appreciation of man, ought to reach to 'man eternal,' man in his simplicity, who hides himself behind all kinds of masks, who runs the risk of involuntarily identifying himself with these masks, thus crippling the saving action of the priest.

By how much the priest fails to reach this man, by so much does he fail to reach man.

This man is the most moving subject of the human story; he is each of us, he is the priest himself, he is the poor actor in the human comedy, who can and must, when that comedy is finished and its décor has been removed, recognise himself for what he is: a man who needs the pardon of Him Who alone can give pardon. A poor man – that is to say, a life which looked on itself as self-possessed, as mistress of itself and of its destiny, imposing itself on others, dominating events, feels itself left to its own resources in a fatal fall into the abyss of death, from which no hand, neither its own nor any other, can save it.

What human sympathy ought the priest to have in order to understand such misery, when that misery is unaware of itself, and to make it his 'own' because he bears it within him, in order thus to prepare for himself a way to the depths in the soul of the sick and the dying.

Though he is sometimes regarded as being as much a stranger as the wounded Jew in the Gospel regarded the Samaritan, the priest must, so to speak, take hold of the sick man, his brother, and lift him up in order that he may bring him to the light which enlightens him, and cause him to recognise in the life that is fading merely the call to a life that is endless, the way to the beatitude which he has until now vainly striven to embrace.

The priest is the most profoundly human of all men – the man who, by his function, knows the meaning of man because he knows what is in man even before the man reveals it to him, since he is the man who knows the meaning of the moral life, the meaning of sin, the meaning of the Light and the Peace destroyed by sin. He is the man who opens the sources of happiness and the avenues to the kingdom of the Beatitudes, not by his own power but by the power which has been conferred on him.

But the priest is also the man who, by his priesthood, is not only a man, but Another Christ – since he has received the powers of Christ and exercises His functions, or rather whose minister he is and through whom Christ exercises His Eternal Priesthood. He is the minister of Jesus of Nazareth, the Christ, the incarnate Son of God, the Priest of the Last Supper; of Him who alone can take away the sins of the world, the Victim who has expiated sins, the King of this kingdom of Beatitude which he came to renew and to open to men, the Christ who has borne all for us – infirmities, sins, miseries, sufferings, death.

He who is the Master of life because He is its Author, and the Master of death because He has conquered it.

This imposes on the priest a function impossible for a man, even for the best among men.

A priest is a priest by the gratuitous choice of Him who, gratuitously, chose His Apostles and His disciples during His mortal life. By that same grace which makes him a priest he can exercise his ministry; he can, through the constant help of Christ who will identify Himself with him, find the strength for the imperious duties which his charge imposes on him.

They will lead him to what every man expects from him, and therefore every patient and every dying person; to this ideal attained by the Abbé Vianney, the priest of a little village called Ars, and which a peasant, who had made a pilgrimage there with many others, expressed simply in answer to a person who asked him on his return: 'What did you see in Ars?' – 'I saw God in a man.'

The same ought to be true of the priest, or at least he should tend towards that ideal, if he wishes to have the knowledge of the sick and the dying, and to find in his fraternal and maternal ingenuity the limitless resources of adaptation which our contemporaries demand.

It remains for us, with infinite respect, to enter into the interior, into the soul of the dying, of the man who is walking more or less slowly towards death, or towards whom death is already approaching to take him into its embrace.

With all patients, with all the dying, there are general traits side by side with particular ones.

The man menaced by a sickness which will finally conquer him, or still more the man already marked with coming death, is a man for whom almost all social activities have ceased. He has been unhooked from the moving train of life, and thinks of himself as run on to a siding, as shunted out of circulation.

Life goes on without him, even that part of which he considered himself an indispensable element. Life goes on – his affairs, his friends, his relations, his family; he who used to weigh up everything now measures nothing but his own impotence. He himself is measured.

If he attempts to stay himself in his fall towards his death, his hands no longer find a gripping-place. When the doctor shall have exhausted his art; when the organism, after renewed resistance, gives way in a retreat which soon changes to a rout, he must realise that he is beaten.

The night of death thickens about the dying man, and his supremely tragic protestation in his agony: 'I want to live and I am dying' – remains without a human answer.

A sad but beneficial consequence of this state is that the warning solitude settling about him is the solitude of the tomb; it is the silence of a world moving away from him, it is the *tête-à-tête* with self; it is self-reflection, possible to the extent to which suffering has not tortured the patient, or his faculties have not been numbed, or the man does not attempt to flee from himself as he has done so often.

The man sees, rising from the depths of his soul, his past, the consequences of his actions, the most external and the most intimate, the public and the secret actions of his childhood, of his youth, together with those of his full maturity and his decline.

He can no longer indulge in outer activity to divert himself; he turns to the interior, and his concern is with himself. He is occupied with his past, and his past occupies him.

It is a chequered past – of happiness and of misery; of honour and of shame; of true love and of love that could not be avowed; of victory and of defeat; of enthusiasm and of disillusion; of duties and of shrinkings; of a Christian life and of a life without God, without faith, without hope.

Misery and splendour; desolate ruins, a place of graves.

Nevertheless, in the distance, the days of his Christian childhood shine with the brilliance of Spring and sing a song whose beauty has been long forgotten.

What a contrast!

Even the best can be gripped by this contrast, and can suffer the to-and-fro tuggings of anguish and of hope.

It is the story of man – the story of God.

For in a backward and single glance, the man who walks towards death discovers, across the story written by himself, the story written by God – the story of the constant goodness of God, the constant goodness of the Father.

In that moment is also born the truth which seeks to realise itself – which does realise itself: it is not God who withholds Himself, His truths, His commandments, His life, His pardon.

He repeats these things to himself as, in the depths of his soul, he reviews the things of God. The priest can help him to discover in the ashes of the past, as the mother does in the dust of the hearth, those sparks of fire that still remain and which will heat the house again.

He can help him gradually or in a flash, according to whether the span of life is to be measured in months, in weeks, in days or in minutes.

Pardon comes at the end – that unique embrace between the Father and the son on the road of life, near to the paternal house, before the threshold is crossed and in order that the prodigal may enter.

It is the joy of the Father and the son, it is the splendour of Easter at the price of the death on Calvary; it is the mystery in the sufferings of the Just for the guilty; it is the mystery of the Cross; it is the meaning of the sufferings of the man who suffers – their value and their transfiguration.

It is the Beatitude of Peace; it is the certainty of a life without end which death cannot take away, but the door of which it opens, since one must die in order to see God.

At the end of these few reflections, we ask ourselves if we have answered the question implied in the heading of the article which is: How ought the priest to approach the dying person?

In order to be complete, it would be necessary to trace the particular features, if not of each dying person, at least of the different spiritual families of the dying, to distinguish and to clarify moral life, religious or irreligious life, milieu, education. But we find assurance in the fact that, when this labour is completed, we must return to the main ideas on which we have attempted to throw light here, in order to describe the conduct of the priest towards the dying. These are the functions of these two men, the doctor and the priest, so near the one to the other; how they ought to understand them and prepare themselves to exercise them; what they are themselves, and what the dying patient is; the interior drama of a life which is dying away; and above all, beside and above the surroundings – more than by different titles – the invisible but present Person of God in the soul and the heart of the doctor or priest and the dying – the invisible Divine Presence in the visible persons.

For in this supreme engagement, the forces to be set in motion and the manner of their employment depend on the obvious preliminary question: What is at issue?

To effect the supreme union with God of the man about to die.

At this height, at this depth – it is all one – the answer to the question of *how* it is to be done remains a difficult one. One must move at once the heart of the man and the Heart of God.

It is necessary to know the one and the Other.

It is necessary to love the one and the Other: to surmount the deep feeling of personal impotence as St. Paul surmounted it when he said:

'I shall glory, therefore, in my weakness, that the power of Christ may dwell in me.'

It is necessary, also, to have confidence in the man who is dying; to doubt him would be to doubt what he is, what is best in him, which he perhaps no longer knows. Made by God, he is made such as he is for God; and God, who has loved him even to giving His Only Son in sacrifice for him, greatly desires him.

More than any of his other ministries, the ministry of the priest to the dying reveals to the priest the infinite mercy of God towards the person who is dying and His very frequently victorious measures to turn him finally to Himself.

P. DIFFINÉ S.J.